THIRD
HARVEST
2021

THIRD HARVEST 2021

Collected Works from
Napa Valley Writers
2021

Prose and poetry from members
of the Napa Valley Writers Branch
of the California Writers Club

Third Harvest 2021

ISBN: 978-0-9985108-3-5
Library of Congress Control Number: 2021922634
Print Edition: December 2021
Managing Editor: Juanita J. Martin
Editors: Sue Kesler, Lenore Hirsch, John Petraglia
Editorial Board: Geoffrey K. Leigh, Bo Kearns, Marty Malin, Gary Orton, Rose Winters, Marilyn Campbell, Amber Lea Starfire, Kymberlie Ingalls, Marianne Lyon, Barbara Toboni
Copyediting: Michael K. Jarvie –www.fixmywords.co.uk
Cover Design: CANDesigner/99 Designs –www.99designs.com
Formatting &Interior Design: Amit Dey –www.in.linkedin.com/in/amitdey1
Published by: Gnarly Vine Press

PO Box 5901
Napa, CA 94581

Foreword

This 2021 anthology is a collection of 59 written expressions by 38 current Napa Valley Writers. The stories, poems, and memoirs are diverse compilations of writing from authors, in various stages of their respective careers. Some are continuing an extensive background of writing, while others are publishing in a collection for the first time. These writings are as unique as the writers themselves. The contents of this book includes suspense, intrigue, humor, love, surprise, reflection, perspective, insight, past and present. These pieces were written for the pleasure of readers, but in addition, these stories can be transformative through shared experiences and connections. Authors write to share, to create, and inform. Along with that process comes the task of placing the words, ideas, and actions in a way that is pleasing to the consumer. This would not have happened without our editors. The editors and their team members spent countless hours examining, and solidifying the writer's words, actions, characters, even their silences, so that the author's words speak to the reader invoking emotional responses and a desire to read their work with endless admiration. Thank you to Sue Kesler, our fiction team editor, Lenore Hirsch, our nonfiction editor, and John Petraglia, our poetry editor, for their leadership and hard work. I also want to extend my gratitude to their team members and other volunteers that shared the workload so that this book would be possible.

—**Juanita J. Martin,** Managing Editor

The past few months I have had the pleasure of being fiction team leader for an exceptional group of caring, thorough editors. In a difficult year, they stepped to the plate to review all manuscripts submitted, checking against a list of criteria, and providing ratings and comments.

I assigned an editor for each submission. They used the team's input to start a two-way dialogue with each author, making suggestions for improvement and inclusion. I want to thank my team members Rose Winters, Gary Orton, Marty Malin, Bo Kearns and Geoffrey Leigh. They are all authors in their own right, having viewed the editing process from the other side. I, too, am an author of five novels. I have also done freelance writing, copy writing, and group critiquing. Enjoy a fine group of stories.

—Sue Kesler, Fiction Editor

These works have had time to breathe and are ready for your reading pleasure. We take you down memory lane to simpler times, country lifestyles, the challenges of school days and survival training, the fun of raising kids, the pain of abuse, dealing with illness, and writer's block. Not to leave out the mysteries of the present-day, there's a homage to driving, a hilarious romp with modern-day technology, and thoughts about how things have changed.

Many thanks to Amber Lea Starfire, Marilyn Campbell, and Kymberlie Ingalls for making my job easy, as well as to the authors, with whom it was a pleasure to collaborate. It is always fascinating to see the variety of stories and styles that writers bring to an anthology. This collection reveals a breadth of human emotion, determination, frailty, and achievement. I hope you enjoy it.

—Lenore Hirsch, Nonfiction Editor

When deciding how to introduce the poems and poets in our new Napa Valley Writers anthology, I thought of many quotes I have come across about poetry, which epitomize the form for me. We all have our favorites. I settled on these two quotes, because they simply and eloquently define the poetry oeuvre and efforts featured in our anthology, Third Harvest.

"There is not a particle of life which doesn't bear poetry within it"

—Gustave Flaubert

"Poetry is a language in which man (woman) explores his (her) own amazement."

—Christopher Fry

Our poets created and deeply commented on a broad range of rare and common particles of life. They shared their insights and amazement, allowing us to think and wonder for ourselves about the world around us. Our poets poetized about: riding a bike through a tunnel; meeting a mountain lion cub on a hike; a coincidental golf pairing; birdsong; aunts; grandfathers; storms; mustard greens; egrets; wildfires; Covid-19; and "I love you" songs, among other compelling poetry-worthy topics. I challenge you to find a life particle pattern here or un-novel amazement that our poets so adeptly lay at our feet for our enjoyment, edification, and aha moments.

I want to thank my collaborators and fine poets Marianne Lyon, Napa's indefatigable Poet Laureate, and Author/Poet, Barbara Toboni, who assisted in reviewing and selecting these 30 poems, to the laudable fountainhead of Third Harvest 2021. Working with them was a pleasurable and collegial celebration of poetry. I also want to thank Juanita J. Martin, Managing Editor, for her support. Finally, to our readers, we hope you enjoy the work of our Third Harvest 2021 poets and look at the world differently because of them.

—**John Petraglia,** Poetry Editor

Acknowledgments

Third Harvest 2021 anthology was truly a group effort. At times, it was a Napa Valley Writers club endeavor.

I volunteered to lead and manage this anthology back in January 2021, at an executive board meeting. On January 13, the Napa Valley Writers board agreed to let me create a third anthology. I wanted to continue the example set by Geoffrey K. Leigh's leadership, as the managing editor of *Meritage*.

This was my first book for Napa Valley Writers. I tapped into my experience as a former editor-in-chief for my college literary magazine, vast publishing credits, and my poet laureateship a decade ago. Although this project was grueling at times, the finished product was worth it.

Unfortunately, this year we were in a global pandemic, which meant we were not able to get together physically. This put some strain on communications and the collaborative process. We did a combination of emails, phone calls, text messages, and Zoom calls to get the work done. At times, a socially distant in-person meeting was necessary.

Nothing would have happened without the work and dedication of our section editors, Sue Kesler, Lenore Hirsch, and John Petraglia. They put in numerous hours on Zoom calls, phone calls, emails, and editing meetings with team members to choose the best writing possible.

I gratefully acknowledge Napa Valley Writers executive board, several of whom I relied on for assistance and guidance.

I also acknowledge the continued support of Geoffrey K. Leigh, who helped me, while writing, editing stories, and working at his job.

In addition, I want to thank Michael K. Jarvie our copy editor, and Amit Dey, who did our book formatting. Our beautiful book cover design concept was envisioned by myself and created by CANDesigner, a Canadian design firm, I found on 99 Designs.com.

I want to especially thank the membership for trusting me with their work. This anthology is comprised of skillful writing from 38 members who contributed 59 pieces of fiction, memoir, and poetry. Their reward is the countless readers who will enjoy their work for lifetimes to come.

—**Juanita J. Martin,** Managing Editor

Introduction

Welcome to the Third Harvest 2021 anthology, comprised of fiction, nonfiction, and poetry. This anthology also introduced a small section of flash fiction, which we hope will become a tradition. We had many join Napa Valley Writers this year from the Napa Valley and the Bay Area, for the excitement and experience of publishing their work. We are still in a pandemic called Covid-19. Despite safe habits and vaccinations, the effects of it linger. We do hope that no matter what is going on in the world, that you the readers will take a literary respite to enjoy these slices of life, imaginary gems, and jewels of our memories.

—**Juanita J. Martin,** Managing Editor

Contents

Fiction:
Let It Breathe

The Dig

Marilyn Campbell

Georgia looked down from her balcony at the fully lit tents two blocks away. They called attention to the figures inside, moving stealthily about—most of them in an unnatural crouch. Working undercover in the middle of the night seemed sinister, eerie, the way the shadows loomed, and then became distorted when team members shifted.

Actually, the scene contained nothing ominous. Some time had passed since Georgia read in the local newspaper that the tents struck on the corner of Silverado and First Street belonged to an archaeology team from a nearby university. They were excavating the site to determine if it had once been a Native American burial ground. Owners of the land could not begin construction on the hotel resort until the team resolved this issue. Several state agencies had rules which prevented such things.

Georgia had learned back in the fourth grade about the Wappo Tribe. These indigenous people of Napa and their villages first lived along creeks or other tributaries. She vaguely remembered that remains of Native Americans were accidentally found in Oakville when the county undertook efforts to restore the Napa River to a more natural state. So, logically, authorities might expect that more bones might be found and authenticated down river near the Oxbow Preserve in Napa.

Georgia wanted to go to bed when she spotted Neosho making his rounds at the site. Since she walked to and from work downtown most days and passed the area, they met one morning near the end of Neosho's nighttime shift as security guard. Georgia stopped to ask about the dig's progress.

He was a storehouse of information and explained that in addition to the property needing a security guard, a Native American monitor must be present during "ground-disturbing work" to protect findings from damage. "I fit the bill for both," he told her.

She watched him now as he checked the gates to make sure they were locked and trained his flashlight around the property's perimeter before moving on. Funny how watching Neosho make his rounds relaxed her. His routine felt like counting sheep to Georgia, lulling her to sleep. So, in spite of her disturbing day at work when her supervisor, Marshall, reprimanded her over how she had handled that day's tour, she retired to bed certain she would sleep. Tomorrow would be a big day for her at the Napa Visitor Company, where she worked as a tour guide. She would be driving a limousine for the first time instead of a van and managing a larger group solo. Up until now, she and Larry, another guide, had teamed up.

The next morning as she walked to work, Georgia was determined to put the unpleasantness with Marshall behind her. Sure, she felt humiliated at being criticized, but still thought she had handled the situation with one of their guests as well as could be expected. She had been concluding the tour when the guest made a provocative comment. What should she have said to him? She went over the scene in her mind again.

"I see that not all is copacetic in the Napa Valley," the casually, but expensively dressed man said.

"How do you mean?" Georgia asked over her shoulder, keeping her eyes on the road.

"Well, I was reading in this morning's newspaper about wineries having problems getting permits—to allow more visitors—like me. Doesn't Napa want to encourage visitors?"

Georgia had been flummoxed on how to answer. This man brought money to the valley. After all, she didn't want him to feel unwelcome. She chose her words carefully.

"There seems to be an ongoing struggle between wine growers to expand and the county's need to control traffic and increase housing. If permits are okayed to add more visitors, it complicates those efforts," she said.

Georgia realized later she should have stopped at this point.

"And, of course, the vintners have also been lobbying to expand their acreage to include eco-sensitive areas. They would like to use their land near streams and to clear-cut trees in the way of planting more vines."

"Oh? Tell me more."

"I have no more to share," she said. *"Except this land of Eden didn't come about easily,"* she laughed.

Soon after their return to the office, Marshall summoned her. Out of the corner of her eye, Georgia saw Larry skulk down the hall.

"Heard you had an interesting day," Marshall said.

"Yes-uh-what do you mean?"

"Sounds like you went beyond show and tell with one of the clients."

"Is that what Larry told you?"

"Larry said the tour was a downer after you voiced your opinion on Napa politics," Marshall said, sharply. "Georgia, we are *not* in the business of politics. What you told our client could have far-reaching negative results."

"What if this man has business ties with the wineries or worse yet, what if he's a freelance journalist who gives Napa a bad name?" Marshall stared at her with his piercing blue eyes.

Georgia stammered. She couldn't come up with a good response. "I'm sorry," she said. "I'll try not to let it happen again."

"I suggest you do more than *try*."

At that point in their conversation, any illusion Georgia had nurtured about getting together romantically with Marshall evaporated. In reality, things had only gone as far as their having drinks after work with co-workers and exchanging some sexual banter. Nothing more.

Georgia shook herself out of the dark mood that threatened to return. She was abreast of the digging site and waved to one of the students.

"Find anything new?" she yelled.

The lanky boy shook his head. "Just a few more arrowheads, is all."

"Well, keep up the good work." She nodded her head and moved on. She pictured the arrowheads and utensils she had seen as part of a collection in Napa's Goodman Library.

After talking with Neosho several times, her curiosity had led her to research further what the Wappo Tribe had left behind of their culture. There were pictures and drawings, of course. Woven baskets of sedge, redbud, and bulrush sat beside obsidian arrowheads arranged behind glass for viewing. But most exciting were the actual pieces of pottery—most were mere shards—whose colors were still brilliant after several hundred years.

She proceeded to buy a small leather notebook in which she listed important dates and the names of tribal leaders, spelling the names phonetically so that she could pronounce them properly. She planned to weave a bit of history into her talks with her wine tour visitors and felt pleasure from the research which went into the effort.

She had tried to share her new passion with co-workers at one of the after-hours get-togethers.

"I find it stimulating. It feels like I'm in school again," she said.

Marshall, who sat two stools away, turned to someone sitting next to him. He muttered under his breath, "If she was so in love with school, she shouldn't have dropped out." His remark stung. But maybe there was some truth to it.

Georgia looked at her watch. She didn't need to compound yesterday's problems with her boss by arriving late to work. She picked up the pace.

As she walked, Georgia couldn't help her mind slipping back to the subject of school and being a student. She remembered being dedicated, not unlike the students at the dig. She had been working toward earning her teaching credential. But in an unguarded moment, she decided to choose adventure over education—an ambition her parents didn't understand. "Stick with school," her father told her. "That should be your first priority."

Instead, she ended up using her savings to join friends on a trip to Europe. "It will broaden my horizons," she explained to her baffled parents. "If I don't go now, I might never get a chance to travel."

She realized later that she should have been wrapping up her senior year and planning her post-graduate work. When Georgia returned from Europe, she was broke. She withdrew from school and picked up work in the Napa hospitality industry. The money was good. The tips, amazing, at times. She told herself that she earned far more money than a teaching credential would ever bring her.

Georgia pulled herself back to the present and saw that she had reached her destination in record time. She arrived at work before anyone else. *Good. That gives me time to go over my notes.*

She would be driving a group of eight visitors from upstate New York in a stretch limo north on Highway 29 and for the return trip to Napa, south on Silverado Trail. *Today,* she thought, *I'm going to give them something extra.*

She took them to the big-name wineries first, including Castello di Amorosa, referred to as "The Castle", and further north to Chateau Montelena. She cooled her heels by the limo while her group received a tour inside the facilities. After stopping at several smaller wineries, her guests had become loud and boisterous. This was okay—even to be expected—but she couldn't afford to wait for stragglers. *There's always one in every group.* Georgia rushed to the tasting room and found her missing guest draped over the bar in an unladylike manner. "Oh!" the woman straightened up. "There you are," she said to Georgia as if *she* were the errant one.

Once they were back on the road, while her guests enjoyed the fall colors on display in rows of crimson and gold-flecked grape vines, Georgia dropped the names of vintners who dominated the industry. She pointed out celebrity summer homes dotting the hills and answered questions about early winemaking. She playfully hinted that production of sacramental wines during Prohibition may have had a "little more kick to them" than federal agents believed. Her guests appeared more entertained with each passing mile. Most had a significant buzz by the time they arrived in Napa.

"Before we conclude our tour," Georgia announced, "I'd like to share with you a little early history of the City of Napa."

She planned on stopping at the excavation site while reciting the history of the Wappo Tribe and their contributions to the Napa Valley. *Local color is what's needed*, she thought.

In the past, when she cited Napa history, she introduced anecdotes about the shady ladies of early Napa by pointing out their long-vacated Queen Anne cottages—also known as "houses of pleasure".

And around Halloween, she dragged out stories of haunted homes in Olde Town as well as a description of the last hanging in Napa next to the courthouse. With stories about a few of Napa's eccentrics thrown in, she usually had their undivided attention. Of course, the wine also helped improve their mood.

"And now, folks, I give you an authentic archaeological dig to observe," Georgia said as she pulled the limo next to the curb on First Street. As she explained what was taking place and the importance of those first indigenous people to populate the Napa Valley, she looked into the rear-view mirror. Georgia noticed the expressions her guests wore varied from amusement to boredom.

"Did the Indians make wine too?" asked the woman, wearing too much perfume. She tittered and someone joined her in laughter.

"That's hard to say," Georgia replied. "The Wappo Tribe may have made wine from available fruit growing here for their elders to drink during ceremonies. But I don't really know that for a fact." She made a note to look it up.

"Bet it wasn't as good as that merlot we had this afternoon," one of the men said.

"Hmm." Georgia frowned. "Well, if there aren't any questions, let's move on." She got the picture. This group was not open to history—to something they couldn't see or touch—or drink. But she thought she'd try one more time.

"If you recall, I pointed out the contributions made by the Chinese. Their construction of wine storage caves and the many rock walls still standing in the county are testament to their skills. They also built other structures." Georgia took a deep breath. "Now we'll drive by one of the oldest stone properties in the area—the original home of the Sam Kee Laundry. Erected in 1875, it is still standing." She raised her voice a notch to emphasize its importance.

She heard a few yawns and felt her blood pressure rise. *That's it!* she thought.

"That concludes our tour today," Georgia said abruptly through clenched teeth.

Georgia was more than disappointed that her experiment had failed. What she thought would be educational fell flatter than a punctured balloon. She would have had better luck teaching her material to a junior high class.

"You shouldn't take this to heart, Georgia," her friend and co-worker said after hearing of the disappointing afternoon. "Most people just want to relax when they come to Napa, not be lectured." Georgia shook her head, but began to realize that as a tour guide, her obligation focused on what customers wanted, not what she thought they should have.

Several days later, on her walk home, as Georgia neared the dig, she noticed a flurry of activity. Excavated holes were being filled in, scaffolding broken down, tents and tools piled to one side. It looked as if they were being assembled for loading into pickup trucks standing by. The site began disappearing as fast as it had sprung up.

"Hey, Neosho, what gives?" she yelled.

He shrugged good-naturedly. "Looks like they're getting ready to close down. Guess they found what they were looking for."

"What's that? What did they find?"

"Couldn't say," he said. "Everything's all hush-hush. You'll have to ask the Suscol Intertribal Council or the bigwigs who plan to build their hotel here. But I think all they found were more small tools, arrowheads—you know—the usual. *But no burial ground!"* He raised his voice and laughed.

"Oh, that's too bad." And then, afraid her remark might be insulting or inappropriate to Neosho, she said, "Well, those other items are important, too."

She had hoped they would find relics of importance which would put Napa on the map—something to talk about besides wine. As long as the students worked the site, the possibility remained of something new being discovered. She gauged her progress against theirs, because she had been digging too—trying to find purpose and joy in her life again. So far, all she had to show for her efforts was an incomplete college education, a failed attempt at romance, and an unfulfilling job.

She wondered how long she would have to continue digging before she found what she was looking for? Maybe not too long. She felt something nagging her, pulling at her, trying to get her attention.

"Thanks Neosho. Hope to see you again, sometime." Georgia pulled her coat tighter against the cold and resumed walking home.

Love and Mercury In Tokyo

Stephen Bakalyar

O n the Tokaido bullet train from Osaka to Tokyo, Paul Cook reviewed his notes and scribbled "accident or murder?" in the margin. His interview with Professor Haru Watanabe at Osaka University had provided little new information about the death of Cook's niece, Alice. Cook had not planned to spend his sabbatical dealing with tragedy, but his skills might solve the mystery of her death.

He glanced frequently at the train's speed meter at the end of the car. When the train reached its top speed of 195 mph, it would be the time of maximum danger. An earthquake and delayed warning signal could conspire to cause a derailment. He knew that the next great quake—expected within thirty years—was unlikely to occur *today.*

But reason was a feeble adversary to his fear. His obsessive-compulsive disorder, a lifelong companion, was at this moment a lively fellow traveler. Meds, therapy, and gritty determination had helped him become a professor of chemistry at the University of Iowa.

He went to the end of the car and made a call.

It was answered after three rings, "Moshi moshi."

"Hi Kate, its Paul."

"Oh Paul, I'm glad you called. I have to stay late at the lab tomorrow, so let's postpone dinner until nine, okay?"

"Sure, that will be fine. Listen, I'm going to extend my visit to Japan. The meeting with Watanabe went poorly. I'm going to go back to Osaka. If you know anyone in the chemistry department, would you see if I can use one of their mass spectrometers next week?"

"I'll ask. What's going on?"

"Watanabe said the coroner thinks Alice might have died of a mercury-based neurotoxin. There were high levels of mercury in her hair. Watanabe inventoried the chemicals in her lab and found no culprit. But he didn't test them, just looked at the labels. I want to see if the contents of the bottles agree with the labels. Maybe they were adulterated."

Silence. "Kate, you there?"

"Yes, Paul, I'm here. I'm thinking that's a far-fetched theory. And if there *is* some bad stuff... well, you'd have to be really careful. I wish you wouldn't do it."

"I know. But I have to find out. I was close to her ever since she was a little girl. And her mother is still broken-hearted. Can you bring gloves and masks to dinner tomorrow? Small vials. A pipette with replaceable tips. Things to help me get samples safely."

"How are you going to get in? Won't her lab be locked?"

"Kate, I arranged it all with Watanabe. Don't worry. I could tell he hated the idea. Gave me reasons why not to do it. But I pushed. He couldn't bring himself to refuse me."

Cook looked at the speed meter. "Kate, I've got to say goodbye. See you tomorrow."

There had been many goodbyes, but none with words of affection. He had kissed her once, as she boarded a subway after they had prowled the neon-lit nightlife of the Roppongi district. A fleeting peck on the cheek.

He bought a bento box and spent the time before arriving at Tokyo Station, eating and keeping an eye on the speed meter.

Four months ago, they had been accidental seat mates on a thirteen-hour flight from Chicago, talking incessantly. He was fascinated by her research into genetics. By the time they were descending toward Tokyo Narita Airport, he had latched onto her bright eyes, her laughter, and her figure, which he scrutinized when she walked to the lavatory. She stirred him like no one else since the death of his wife. He had learned that she was divorced and had coaxed a phone number from her. They spent four days sightseeing together during his week-long visit to Japan. After staying only three weeks back in Iowa, he had now returned to Tokyo, determined to woo her.

As he dressed for their dinner date, worries jostled for position. Had divorce left her leery about marriage? Did she have reservations about his being sixty, eight years her senior? Would she ever return to the States? Six months remained in her contract, but she had let him know how much she had fallen in love with Japan. Her spoken Japanese was adequate for a permanent research environment or a teaching position in a university with degree programs offered in English.

As Kate dressed, she too was worried. She was at a crossroads—follow Paul's lead to intimacy, or tell him that they would remain just friends? She looked in the mirror. What would it say to him that she wore a black wrap dress that accentuated her trim five-foot-nine figure? What was it saying to herself?

Paul took a subway to the Shibuya district and walked to the small restaurant Kate had chosen. She was sitting at one of the five small tables in the dimly lit restaurant, typical of the interesting places she found for their adventures.

"Hi, Kate. Here, let me take that." He put the bag next to his chair.

"I brought quite a lot. I hope it's everything you'll need to stay safe."

"Thanks. Kate, I know you're worried. I'll be careful. The more I think about my talk with Watanabe, the more I wonder if he is hiding something from me." He saw a frown come over Kate's face. "OK, no more about that. What about dinner? You've been here before, right?"

"You won't be disappointed."

"Kate, let's have sake. Get the good stuff. Make tonight special."

She gave him a quizzical look. Then her smile fortified his courage. He had resolved to move the relationship forward.

She spoke to the waiter, who returned with a porcelain bottle and small porcelain cups. Kate poured the warm liquid into Paul's cup. "It's tradition to serve each other."

Paul poured her cup, raised his, and said "Kampai."

She raised hers. "Cheers."

When they had finished eating, Paul refilled her cup. As she reached for the bottle, he intercepted her hand and held it in both of his. "Kate, we haven't known each other very long. But I'm incredibly attracted to you. If there is a chance, a possibility, you could come to feel that way about me, then I want us to spend a lot of time together before I leave Japan."

Her eyes drifted down to their hands.

Paul pressed on. "There wouldn't be much time. I'll have to analyze those samples, and irrespective of the results, I will return to Iowa in a week. But if we could spend evenings together before I leave, it would be wonderful."

He paused again. No response. "I guess I should stop talking."

He released her hand, but Kate quickly grasped his and looked up. "Paul, it's been a long time since I have enjoyed myself so much with someone. There is no denying I have affection for you. Could it go beyond this? I don't know. But I think spending more time together is a good idea. Let's do it and see what happens." She poured the remaining sake into his cup.

"I have an idea. I have some time off coming. Why don't I go to Osaka with you? Help you get samples. We could take a side trip to Kyoto. I'd love to show you the Katsura Imperial Garden. It is incredible."

When Paul saw her onto the subway that night, he was cautious, but Kate pulled him to her and gave him a lingering kiss. It surprised them both.

Two days later, on the train to Osaka, Paul said, "I guess you've noticed I have some strange mannerisms."

"Yes."

"I have obsessive-compulsive disorder, OCD. Does it bother you?"

"Not at all. Does it bother *you*? I mean, what is it like?"

"When I was young, it was tough. My parents didn't understand. By the time I was in graduate school, I had learned to cope. But difficult thoughts are always just around the corner. For example, I chose this seat because it faces away from the speed meter." He turned and pointed. "If I faced it, and it caught my eye, I would spend the trip repeatedly checking. It would trigger a fear that the train will derail in an earthquake."

"So how do you feel about the risk of collecting the samples?"

"I'm not concerned—about the actual work. What I *am* uneasy about is what to do if I find mercury contamination. I asked Watanabe about Alice's social life. He said she had no relationships with other students. But her mom said Alice's letters mentioned boyfriend problems. If it *was* murder—my god, that's the first time I have said that word out loud—if it was, it would take some intense detective work. I sure can't do it. Since the police already investigated, I doubt a request from me, an outsider, would be welcome."

Kate said, "If you find something, we can come up with a plan. For now, let's just get the samples, then enjoy Kyoto."

Paul checked his watch as the train came to a stop at the Osaka station. "There has been a screw-up. Eight seconds early." They laughedand retrieved their bags. They checked into a hotel near the university.In the morning, at Watanabe's office, Paul introduced Kate. "Good morning, professor. This is doctor Bishop. She will assist me in collecting samples."

Watanabe nodded. He stood and handed Paul a key. "Room 217. If I am not in when you finish, leave this on my desk."

They both put on lab coats, gloves, and face masks. Paul lined up the bottles of chemicals, put a numbered paper in front of each, then took photographs of each bottle and its number. He labeled the sample collection vials with corresponding numbers.

He turned to Kate and said, "Are you familiar with the death of the Dartmouth chemist a few years ago? She spilled a drop of dimethyl mercury on her glove. In a few weeks, she noticed weight loss. Then came balance problems and slurred speech. She died within a year. Until that happened, no one knew it could penetrate latex gloves."

"No, I don't remember that. But thanks for increasing my anxiety."

"Sorry. It's an incredibly potent neurotoxin. Watch me like a hawk. Speak up if you see anything that suggests I've made a spill. In that case, tell me what you saw, then stand aside and let me handle it."

He adjusted the fit of his mask, removed it, and repeated the fitting three times. Paul was collecting the last sample when the door opened a crack.

Kate turned and said in Japanese, "Hello. Can I help you?" There was no reply. She repeated, "Hello." Finally, a young man took one step inside. He stared at them. The three were frozen in silence. Then he spun around and hurried away.

"That was weird," she said.

Paul checked that the vial caps were secure and said, "Let's get out of here."

At the Katsura Garden, they sat silently on a bench overlooking the central pond. Breeze-driven ripples glided toward them, forming bands of green and blue, reflections from the distant forested hill and the cloudless sky.

Kate reached over and took Paul's hand. "So, Paul, I have two suitors. You and this amazing country. We've had good times in the city. I wanted you to see another face of Japan." They kept their gaze on the lake. "Over three hundred years ago, when the princes lost power to the ruling shoguns, they pursued the art of garden design. This is one of three Imperial Gardens. Today they are reverently preserved."

Paul said, "And here we are, beneficiaries of their reverence. You've been to the other gardens?"

"Yes. This is my favorite. Come on, let's walk." They stopped frequently along the paths, Kate pointing out the artistry of the distant views framed by meticulously manicured trees and shrubs.

As they left the garden, Paul said, "This has been wonderful. You know, you perceive and value what I don't even notice. It sounds corny, but you bring beauty to my life."

"That's good to hear, Paul. I did think you would enjoy this." She turned to him. "What you bring to *my* life, Paul, beyond the enjoyable things we do together, is an appreciation of your character. You have an unwavering determination to track down what happened to your niece. I have not known a man with such tenacity for seeking justice. I like it." On a late train to Tokyo, she slept with her head on his shoulder.

The next day, Paul called her. "Watanabe just phoned me. One of his grad students came to him, sobbing and nearly incoherent. He didn't explicitly confess to adulterating the chemicals, but Watanabe thought it a possibility. He referred him to a psychiatrist. I'm guessing the student was the guy who looked in on us when we were getting samples. Maybe he thought we were police. I told Watanabe I'd let him know the results of my analysis."

"My god, Paul. Your suspicion might be right. So now there really *could* be bad stuff in those vials. Be careful."

After two days of waiting for access to a mass spectrometer, it took only an afternoon to find traces of dimethyl mercury in five of the samples. He told Kate and Watanabe and caught the first available flight back to Iowa. After several days with his sister, waiting to hear from Kate, a text message arrived: "A lot has happened. I consulted a lawyer. He thinks everything points to murder and that the grad student is the likely perpetrator. Hearing of your mass spec results, Watanabe notified the police. The Osaka prosecutor has opened a criminal investigation and wants to talk to you. He will also probably contact your sister.

"The student is under psychiatric care and has a restraining order keeping him in Osaka. Congratulations, Paul."

He was about to reply, when another text came. "I miss you. Come soon. I've decided to return to the States when my contract is over."

Good Samaritan

Lenore Hirsch

He was hurtling along lonely River Road in a beat-up Ford pickup, enjoying the blast of cool air from his window, when he spotted the car. It was parked off to the side under a shedding maple. A red-clad figure stood next to the car. Sam let up on the accelerator to check it out.

That Saturday morning in September, Sam Goodwin was on a schedule. Julia wanted to have everything delivered, but Sam insisted he would pick up from the florist, deli, and bakery. He wanted to keep busy, to keep dark thoughts from overtaking his brain and pushing his spirit into a miserable corner. As Sam slowed, he saw it was a woman in a red coat. Hands on hips, she studied the flat tire. Screams bellowing from the back seat suggested a toddler.

He had no interest in stopping to help a stranger. Surely, she could call AAA or a friend on her cell phone. Gone were the days of folks stranded for hours without a way to call for help. Sam would never get a prize for being the friendly, outgoing sort. He had heard himself described as gruff, like a big, cranky bear. Not much of a talker. The woman looked up as he applied the brakes.

The service would begin in two hours, and he needed to get home in time to arrange furniture and change clothes. But despite his cranky demeanor, Sam had a soft spot for ladies in distress. That included moms with screaming children. Not that he'd had much experience with kids since Joanna was little. He left all the tough stuff to Julia back then—diapers, skinned knees, spats with playmates. But his reluctance for hands-on parenting didn't stop his heart from hurting when Joanna was suffering.

OK, don't think about Joanna, he told himself. *Nothing good will come from that.* He ground the brakes to a halt in front of the disabled car and climbed out of the truck.

"Hi, ma'am. Flat tire?"

"Yes," she answered, with a wary look.

"No AAA?" he asked.

"No, I never got around to doing that. Guess I should. Used to be if I had car trouble, I'd just call my dad, and he'd come and bail me out, even from an hour away." She paused, looked at the ground. "But he passed away last spring, and this is the first time—"

"No worries, I can give you a hand. Why don't you take care of that little one. Show me the spare and I'll fix it for you in no time."

Sam removed his jack from the truck and bent to work on the tire while the young woman released the little boy from his seat and walked him around in the dry grass covered with red and orange leaves. Fifteen minutes later, as Sam tightened the lugs on the spare tire, she approached, holding the boy.

"Thanks so much. I really appreciate it."

"Yep, no problem." The child looked at Sam with interest. Wide blue eyes, open mouth, scent of baby powder. He wore a blue puffy jacket. *Pretty darn cute. Is he studying my mustache? Or the baseball cap?*

"I'll be sure to join AAA when I get home."

Sam couldn't think of anything else to say. He took the boy's hand and gave it a squeeze, noting the smooth skin and tiny grasping fingers. Sam returned the jack to his truck, wiped his hands on his pants, and waved goodbye.

"You have a great day now," she called out, as she strapped the toddler back into his seat. Sam continued on his way, picked up the items they needed for the reception, and headed back the way he had come. The young woman and her car were gone. He wondered where she was going. *Could have asked*, he thought. *Clearly, she's from out of town*. But those were thoughts Sam often had *after* an encounter, when it was too late.

Back home, Julia wanted to know. "What took you so long? I was starting to worry."

"Stopped to help a stranded young woman," he answered. "My good deed for the day."

Julia, in her black dress, looked pale and grim, but her half-smile acknowledged his kindness. "Better change," she said.

A half hour later, Sam and Julia arrived at the cemetery chapel and slowly made their way to the room where Joanna's funeral was about to begin. They were greeted by long-time friends in the town that had been home since they married, the town where their daughter grew up. They welcomed a few of Joanna's friends from high school, but her current buddies were stuck halfway across the planet in a war zone, trying not to end up like Joanna.

Sam awkwardly accepted condolences from the two uniformed military officers who were in attendance to honor his daughter. Julia easily found things to say to them. "Thank you for coming. . . it would mean a lot to Joanna. . . we're honored to have you."

Escaping to the designated row in the front, Sam sat before the flag-draped coffin and two standing displays of red and white roses. He studied the program Julia had created. For the millionth time, he tried not to think of his only child, his baby girl, blown up by an IED. Her first tour in the army. After success at the university, with infinite possibilities for the future, she did the patriotic thing and joined up. *The young have no idea what can befall them at any moment*, Sam thought.

Julia wept quietly by his side during the speeches, while Sam struggled in silence to contain his emotions—he had no desire to talk.

One of Joanna's high school girlfriends told a story about their teenage antics.

The sounds of soft chuckles and crying from the assemblage stirred Sam's memories of raising a headstrong girl. At the end of the service, Julia wiped her eyes and stood before the crowd of forty friends. She thanked everyone for coming and invited them to the reception at their home, following the short burial service. The two military officers assisted Sam and several family friends in carrying the coffin out into the autumn sunlight, the other mourners drifting out behind them.

The officers removed the flag, folded it ceremoniously, and handed it to Julia. Standing next to her at the open grave, Sam finally looked up. A smaller group than in the chapel, about twenty people remained, some standing close and some at a distance. Sam, at first, questioned his perception when he noticed a young woman in a red coat standing in the back. It was the woman with the flat tire. The boy was again in her arms, but wriggling, trying to get free. She made eye contact and nodded.

How could this be? What a coincidence for the woman to be here. She knew Joanna? He hadn't asked her business in town, but still . . .

As the coffin was lowered, Sam tossed his handful of dirt and listened to the wistful recording of a solitary bugle playing taps. Guests came up to him before departing, shook his hand and murmured regrets. He said thanks to each one, while he watched the woman in red struggling to keep her little boy from running wild. He thanked the military officers, then said to Julia, "I'll be right back," and marched towards the young mother.

She walked towards her vehicle, following the boy, who ambled in the slow, tipsy way that toddlers do. Sam quickened his step. "Wait," he said.

She turned to face him. "Hi again."

"You knew Joanna?"

"Yes."

"Look," he said, gazing back at his car, "please come to the house. I'd like you to meet Julia, my wife. And we could talk. It's 210 Willow Street."

"OK." The little boy reached to be picked up by his mother, making urgent, wordless noises. She hoisted him up, and he immediately fastened his eyes on Sam with the same enchantment as earlier in the day.

"Turn right back on Main St. and then it's your next left." For the first time that day, Sam felt tears fill his eyes. He'd been holding them in for too long. He wiped his face with his bare hand.

"OK, we'll be there."

He turned back to Julia and the lingering guests. After saying goodbye to the last person, he walked Julia to their car and settled himself in the driver's seat. "You won't believe this," he said. "That's the woman I stopped to help this morning. She came to town for the funeral."

"Oh . . . did you get her name? Is she coming to the house?"

"No, but, yes, she said she'd come."

Back at the house, Sam and Julia moved with numb efficiency, removing trays of food from the refrigerator and uncapping bottles of wine and water. Sam opened the sliding door to the patio, so folks could spread out. Their friends dribbled in a few at a time, filled plates and found a place to sit. At last, there was the woman in the red coat.

"I think I'm rather late on introductions," said Sam, and gave her his name.

"I'm Anita . . . Anita Gleeson. And this is Johnny."

"I still can't get over the fact that I met you by accident this morning."

"I should have told you why I was in town."

"I should have asked!" Julia joined them and Sam introduced the two women.

Johnny started to fuss. "He's tired. It's past his nap time," said Anita.

"Let's see if we can find a place to put him down," offered Julia.

Anita followed Julia and Sam into the spare bedroom, Joanna's old room. The two women arranged a beanbag chair on the floor into a safe sleeping platform and set Johnny down. He was already nodding off as they chatted about his age and Anita's home an hour away.

"So how did you know Joanna?" asked Sam.

"In college. I lived down the hall from her in the dorm and we sometimes hung out late at night. She was there for me when I was going through a tough time."

"Nice to meet you," said Julia. "I've got to get back to the other guests, but I hope we can talk later."

"Me too," said Anita, as Julia turned to leave.

Sam wanted to know more. "We didn't meet many of her college friends. They lived far and wide, as I recall."

"Well, I want you to know that Joanna talked about you. About growing up here. The challenges of being an only child and all the time you and her mom spent keeping her active. The sports, music lessons, the family board games. I remember her telling me, and she made air quotes with her fingers and did a poor imitation of Joanna's husky voice, *My dad doesn't show much emotion, but he has a heart of gold.*"

Sam's eyes spilled his bottled-up grief like spring water after a heavy rain.

"Sorry," she said. "I didn't mean to upset you."

"You're not . . . it's OK . . . thank you."

"She was a deep thinker and a good friend," Anita said. "I'm sorry that I didn't keep in touch after we graduated. It's such a loss."

Sam looked into Anita's eyes that glistened with tears. He wanted to know more, but couldn't think of anything to ask. "Let's join the others," he said.

They returned to the guests and the food. Sam took a few minutes in the bathroom to pull himself together and then made the rounds of his longtime friends. After an hour, the guests started to take their leave, and Sam watched as Anita went to retrieve Johnny. They came out of Joanna's room smiling, the little boy full of life after his nap.

As Johnny jumped up and down, making loud car noises, Anita laughed. "He's a handful. His father left me early on; there was nobody to look after him today, so I had to bring him along. I'm sorry if he's been a disturbance."

Julia knew what to say. "He's no problem. We're so glad you both came."

Anita and Julia said goodbye, and it was Sam's turn. Something important was making a knot in his stomach and quickening his breath. "I'm sorry we didn't have more time to talk," he said.

"Would you hold him for a minute?" and she offered Johnny to Sam. He took the boy into his arms and Johnny immediately reached for Sam's mustache, trying to grab it with that tiny hand. It had been a long time since Sam had held a toddler. It brought back memories of another little one's tactile explorations.

"Whoa, little guy," said Sam as he bounced Johnny in his arms.

Anita rummaged in her big purse, extracting a pen and a scrap of paper. She wrote on it and held it out. "I'll trade you," she said.

Sam handed Johnny over and took the paper with her phone number on it.

"If you'd like to talk, I'd like that," she said and put her free hand on his arm, giving it a squeeze.

"I definitely would."

"Both of us," said Julia.

Sam continued, "Be sure to get that tire fixed now. Don't leave the spare on too long."

Anita smiled.

Little Johnny and Anita walked down the sidewalk into the brisk autumn air. Sam Goodwin stood holding the slip of paper, and for the first time in weeks, felt a glimmer of hope.

Taylor Camp

David Kerns

an excerpt from *Max's Music*,
a novel-in-progress

"Ya been here before?" the driver asked.

He said it with a smirk, not an ominous smirk, but mischievous, like Max was in for a happy surprise. Which he was.

Max had hitchhiked all the way from the airport, three drivers' worth, this particular one picking him up in Hanalei, the funky beachside town that would contain the rest of his life.

Dropping Max, his two big duffels, a backpack and his guitar case, the driver said aloha and Max said thank you and the driver said mahalo and Max said, "What?"

"Mahalo," the driver said, "that's how you say thanks in Hawaii."

"Okay, mahalo."

"De nada, man."

That last leg was a jeep ride, open air and fragrant. Max didn't know what he was smelling, but it sure wasn't Chicago, which he'd departed only that morning. They snaked back and forth between the ocean's edge and the land side, with its dense, green tropical overhang. The road, narrow to start with, was punctuated by one-lane bridges. Max wondered what the rule was when two oncoming vehicles arrived at precisely the same moment.

His Samaritan slowed down to show him a yawning separation between a rock face and the ground, the mouth of a cave that he told him was popular with the tourists. Max could see six hippie-types seated in a circle near the entrance. About fifty yards further was where the driver stopped, taught him how to express gratitude like a local, and disgorged him and his earthly belongings.

"Which direction?" Max asked. "TAYLOR CAMP."

"You go through there," the driver said, pointing at a grove of palm trees. "Just walk toward the surf," whose distant music Max had not appreciated until just then.

"Taylor Camp is over there?"

"You can't miss it," the driver said, mischief still animating his face.

Max took stock of his stuff, which was now covered in a thin layer of red dust, and realized that his clothes were similarly decorated. Sitting on one of the duffels, the one without the record albums and cassettes, he took a long swig of water from his canteen and pulled the postcard from the back pocket of his jeans. He unfolded it and read it for maybe the thirtieth time.

Dearest Max
Come to Kauai, to Hanalei, to Taylor Camp
We should be together
Skye

The front of the postcard was an idyllic vista—ascendant tropical mountainsides with blue ocean below and even bluer sky above. The diagonal decorative script read, "Napali!"

He'd had it for about a month, kept it in that back pocket. He probably wouldn't have come— it was kind of crazy—if his boss at the record store hadn't been such an asshole. The man thought he knew more than everybody. He insisted that the Byrds' "Sweetheart of the Rodeo" was "country crap". This, Max thought, was heresy. And he accused Max of lying when he told him how John Prine came in one day and they talked for an hour, talked about Steve Goodman and Kristofferson and the Old Town School of Folk Music and all that.

The last straw, though, the thing that finished it off, was this fight they had in front of a customer. It was stupid, but the boss had gotten under his skin one too many times. This girl came in and asked Max to recommend a Dylan album. It had been years since the release of *Blonde on Blonde*, but Max was raving about it. Bossman came over and, right in front of the girl, said to Max, "Don't be ridiculous," and said to her, "Don't listen to him. He doesn't know what he's talking about." It was then that Max tipped over the entire bin of Golden Oldies, 1940-1960, while screaming pretty much every obscenity in his vocabulary. It was shortly after that, of course, now unemployed, that he decided that Skye and the island of Kauai could perhaps do him some good.

It was about a hundred yards to the palm grove and, not wanting to leave anything behind, Max was trying to figure out how to get his stuff over there in a single trip. He would let go of his big city paranoia soon enough, but this was the first day of the rest of his life as an islander, and he wasn't giving up 24 years of urban vigilance at the drop of a coconut. The backpack and the two duffels, as heavy as they were, were manageable. The problem was the guitar.

The Martin D-28, as prized a possession as any he owned, was in a heavy hard-shell case. He tried it under his arm while hauling everything else and it twice fell to the ground, which was exactly two times more than should happen in the entire lifetime of that exquisite instrument.

A Hawaiian-looking boy, maybe ten- years- old, was kicking a beach ball around the sandy, grassy patch separating Max from his destination. He offered the boy a quarter to help him with the guitar and the kid happily bounded over.

The case was heavy, but he managed it, holding the handle with two hands, carrying it crosswise in front of him, as they silently headed for the grove.

The boy stopped just short of the trees, put the case on the ground and said, "I can't go in there."

"Why not?"

He looked away, but Max could see that he was fighting a smile. "I can't," he said, "mama says I can't."

"I don't understand," Max said. "It's just palm trees."

Now the kid's got his hand in front of his mouth, unsuccessfully suppressing a giggle. "Susus."

"What? What are you saying?"

He repeated it, this time louder. "Susus."

"I don't know what that means."

The boy turned, looked Max dead in the face and said, "Titties."

Max was, of course, expecting a nude beach on the far side of the grove, and there was one, though he couldn't yet see it. What he did see looked like something out of a *National Geographic* spread about, say, Borneo. Tree houses. There were dozens of houses constructed of what looked like bamboo connected to hardwood tree trunks. Some were small and simple, some elaborate, with multiple-laddered levels and horizontal extensions. The roofs were veils of thick plastic canted every which way.

"Hey there," a man said. "Aloha." At first, Max couldn't locate him.

"You need some help?" the man said, emerging from behind one of the structures on Max's left. He looked like an extra in a Polynesian movie, one of the guys who paddled out to meet Marlon Brando in *Mutiny on the Bounty*. He wore only a brightly flowered sarong. His skin was the color of a copper penny, his defined upper body degenerating into a beer belly. He had the hair of a holy man, wavy and white to his shoulders, and months of beard to match. He was smiling.

"I could use some help, yes, uh, Mahalo. I'm Max."

"My name is Warren," he said, "but everybody calls me Ray, like manta ray."

"This is Taylor Camp, yes?"

"Yeah man, this is it," he said, "the last resort, the end of the surf bum, hippie scum trail. You found it all right, but you don't really seem like either.'"

This hurt a little. Surf bum was preposterous, but what exactly disqualified Max from hippie respectability? What, that he wasn't a patchouli stink bomb? His asshole boss at the record store told him three times a week that he looked like a dirty hippie. He was never dirty; the man just didn't like the hair and the clothes. And his sandals, he especially didn't like his sandals. What the hell was a straight judgmental prick like him doing in the record business, anyway?

"I was invited here by a girl," Max said. "You must know her; her name is Skye."

Something shifted in Ray. An increment of buoyancy dialed back, a minute hesitancy in his response. Max's immediate thought was that Ray was screwing her.

"Skye's a good friend," Ray said. "She knows you were coming today?"

"Actually, no."

"Come on. I'll help you with your stuff and we'll go find her. She lives in the Big House, beachfront property." Ray grabbed both duffels like they were weightless, and Max followed with the backpack and the guitar.

The camp was bigger and more elaborate than he had imagined. They passed at least a dozen tree houses on the right, each an obvious improvisation, different sizes and shapes dictated by terrain and vegetation and need. After several more on the left, there was a complex with a toilet, a shower and some kind of makeshift hot water factory using two big oil drums. Beyond that, there was a vegetable garden that occupied at least a half-acre.

Two entirely naked women holding hands walked past Ray, briefly greeting him. Max feigned disinterest. There was nothing un-cooler than staring. He wasn't completely inexperienced with public nudity. There was plenty of it at Woodstock, which was, by the way, where he first met Skye.

Now the surf was loud, and Max could see the ocean between the remaining tree houses ahead of them. Thirty more yards and they were on the sand.

A stream coming from their right spilled into the ocean. He asked Ray about its source. "It's rainwater from that mountain behind us," he said. "Officially, it's Limahuli Stream, but everyone just calls it the river. Nice for a cold dip."

He'd seen the Pacific Ocean before, in California, but it didn't look like this. In California it was blue-ish. The Atlantic that he'd seen in New England was slate gray, and Lake Michigan, the "ocean" of his childhood, was green and inhospitable, a place where lamprey eels might suck out your eyeballs. The Pacific here was really blue, and turquoise, like the Caribbean in spots.

At the moment, it was peacefully living up to its name.

"Let's go over there," Ray said. "That's the Big House."

It was large side-to-side, and closer to the ground than many of the other structures, which was fine with Max and his acrophobia. There was a sort of annex on one end that was more elevated than the rest, but most of the platform was just four or five feet above the sand. A wooden stairway with five steps, dead center facing the beach, was the way in.

He asked Ray how many families lived in there. "Three with kids," he said. "It's pretty communal. Everybody takes care of everybody's kids. It works."

Ray called up and asked for Skye. A heavily bearded man in a sombrero stepped out of the entrance and said she was around, but he didn't know where.

Max realized that he needed to get away from Ray. He'd been kind and hospitable, but even if there were no complicating connection between him and Skye, he wanted his reunion with her to be pure, private, just the two of them. He'd come thousands of miles for this young woman and this experience. An awkward start, some triangular weirdness, seemed possible, maybe even likely.

"Hey, Ray," he started. "Thanks for your help. I really appreciate it. I'm gonna walk the beach, take all this in. I'd kinda like to be by myself. I hope you don't mind. Just want to be by myself with it."

"That's very cool, man. I completely dig it. Enjoy."

"Thanks, man. Mahalo."

He'd spent only six days of his life with Skye—three at Woodstock in '69 and three in Chicago in '70. There were a couple of love letter-ish flurries, occasional postcards, several months between, and then, a year later, the Taylor Camp invitation. That was it. But something happened at Woodstock, something authentic and apparently indelible. Yeah, it was fueled by pot and acid and hot sex, but there was obviously more. And it was so familiar and easy when she visited in Chicago. Crazy, maybe, but the thread connecting them seemed to be immune to space and time. He felt it, and it seemed like she did, too.

It was nice to stroll the beach alone, his feet in the Pacific. There were scattered folks out there, some in the water and some out, some nude, some partially or fully bathing-suited. Men, women, kids. There was a volleyball game going on a little down the way, four naked guys, four sets of cocks and balls freely flopping this way and that. It didn't look that comfortable.

He'd barely arrived, and he was already adapting to the nudity. There was no arousal. The blood was not rushing to his loins, or seemingly to anyone else's either. What's really the big fucking deal, anyway? The human race spent a whole lot of its history before deciding to cover up. The rest of the animal kingdom isn't apparently embarrassed. What's our problem?

From where he was standing, the beach extended a long way to the west. He began a slow stroll in that direction, on one level taking in everything, on another scanning for Skye, looking ahead, occasionally looking back. From a great distance, she wouldn't be obvious. There were a few possibilities, but they were quickly disqualified.

Almost at the end of the westbound part of the beach, before it bent to the south, a young woman, the right height and shape, was walking toward him. He could tell she was dark-haired like Skye, and she was walking alongside and holding hands with a little girl. The closer she got, the more certain he was. It was Skye, all right, and she hadn't recognized him yet. He stopped walking and just waited.

When she was about fifty yards away, she seemed to notice him, and he waved. She waved back and broke into a run, at least a jog that the kid could keep up with. He reciprocated, and they met in what must have looked like a pretty corny romantic collision. They hugged and pecked and mumbled their hellos. He wasn't going to drop her to the sand a la Burt Lancaster in front of some Taylor Camp kid.

When they settled down, Skye said, "Max, this is my daughter, Lani. Honey, this is Max."

He'd never even considered it.

Daniel

Kymberlie Ingalls

"I was named after the Elton John song," Daniel said. They sat side by side on the curb. He watched sideways as Lindsay tugged at her sweater and felt bad that he didn't have a jacket with him to offer. The hem of her skirt rustled against her long legs. "Dad would sing it to my mother at his shows. Then one day he up and disappeared just afore I turned ten. Ma said she wanted me to see the world through wide-open eyes. She'd say 'you're a star in the face of the sky, don't you never forget that.'" He was pleased at Lindsay's slight smile but could see the loneliness behind it. He kept his eyes downward as he wrapped the blue twine in and around his fingers before he unwound it again.

The light from the lamp cast aged yellow rays over the broken sidewalk. He pulled at the errant grass that grew where the concrete had broken apart. It was another cool spring evening in another small town that wasn't any different from any other small town in the Midwest. Only the names of the parades and festivals distinguished them as one made one's way across the mountains and valleys.

Daniel wasn't from this town, but he'd been here so long that folks didn't remember that. Ma had run off to chase after a song but sent him back home as a teen for some grounding before she passed on. It didn't take long for a string of labor jobs to take him across different highways for the better part of two decades. With only a beaten down Chevy truck to his name, he returned to the family farm to help out around the place. After Granddad died, and no family to speak of, the place was sold with barely enough to cover the debt. Daniel was left with enough to rent a room at the residence motel behind the main road, until the money ran dry. It wasn't so bad. The burden of rent didn't weigh him down anymore. Sometimes he'd drive out to the old man's pasture just off the highway at the end of town and park there for the night, settling in the bed of the truck on an old mattress and would lie there, wandering through his head to figure things out. Thirty-six years old, not tied to anything in the world. A new family lived there now. They didn't seem to mind. The young girls would even bring him a warm breakfast now and again, as their parents waved from the kitchen window.

Something had been gnawing at his gut, though. He wasn't entirely certain when it started. Just woke up one day and felt it piled into the bottom of his stomach. One night last week, he'd been sitting inside the tavern in the middle of town, when Lindsay had walked in. Everyone knew how she paid her bills, and most men in the room had donated to the cause, but nobody knew who the daddy was to that little boy she was raising. She'd come here some years back from another small town and didn't keep with the women too much. During the day, she could be seen on her front porch, sitting in the shade with a book or playing in the yard with the boy, at their quiet bungalow home. Sometimes when he strolled past on one of his walks, Daniel would catch a smile on her pretty face.

For some reason that he couldn't put a name to, when Lindsay walked into the bar that night, the rock in him got bigger and heavier. Daniel thought maybe it was because she was the only other person who didn't seem to belong, either. Or maybe he was tired of his own self and his ways. There wasn't even a good reason he never stayed with a job for more than a few weeks, but the only thing anyone offered anymore were day jobs that gave him enough for a meal.

Some nights, he'd clean up the bar and the owner would let him pick over the snacks that hadn't sold. Every so often, someone's wife would send a home cooked meal in for him with their husbands.

Daniel didn't feel disliked by anyone, but never talked to anyone about the things he wished he could. Tonight, he heard himself saying those things to Lindsay.

He'd just been sitting here, looking down the empty road, and heard her behind him leaving the tavern alone. There was a pause in her steps. "Hello." Her voice was soft. "What's got you out here all alone at midnight?"

"Best time to think." Daniel felt like a dumb, shy schoolboy.

"Do you mind?" Lindsay pointed at the curb next to him when he looked up at her. He shrugged as if he would have considered saying no. They talked into the hour without interruption, as everyone else had made their way home with bellies full of beer.

"May I ask you something?" *Damn,* he thought. *She just sounds so smart. Even when she's not saying much at all.* He raised his green eyes to her river-blue ones. Her hair made him think of a frosted strawberry lemonade on a country day, and he wanted so badly to touch it right then. Instead, he skimmed his own blonde shag with a nervous hand. "Often I see you with this blue string. What does it represent to you?"

He felt surprised that she'd noticed him before this and fumbled around for his words. "Well, this town I was in, I don't even remember when, one day, I'm sitting outside a restaurant and this kid was there with his mama. He didn't have any hair on his head, not even above his eyes. Real thin and sickly.

But he had the biggest laugh every time this dog out on the sidewalk wagged its tail or slurped at someone passing by. I watched him pull out this little ball of blue string from his pocket, and he cut off a piece with a butter knife. Tied a note I'd watched him write to the arm rail of the chair and they left." Daniel paused, closing his eyes in remembrance.

"I had to know, so I walked over and read it: *Tomorrow I may not be here, but today I was. This blue string ties us together. Smile, you were here today too.*" Daniel stopped and stared at Lindsay, wondering if she wanted him to go on. She nodded at him. "Ever since then, I carry a ball of blue string with me." He pulled it out to show her. "I think about that kid a lot. Whenever I do, I tie a piece of this here string to something. A tree, a chair, a street post. Anywhere. I don't know, I guess because maybe I want people to know I was there too."

Lindsay leaned forward a little to take his hand in hers and fingered the string he'd wrapped again around his finger. "That's lovely, Daniel. Thank you for sharing that with me."

He kicked at the street. "Look, you're a real sweet lady." he began. "I don't know how to ask this…"

"Just ask me."

"Well, I think you're real pretty. And you've been so nice to sit here with me. I ain't got anywhere to go tonight but that lonesome truck of mine." He reached into the pocket of his old jeans and pulled out the last dollar he had. "You're worth a million of these, Lindsay, but I wondered if I gave this to you, maybe you'd let me kiss you here in the moonlight." He pressed the crumpled bill into her palm.

Lindsay was silent for the longest time, her face tilted down from his. "I sure like you too." Her voice was like a summer song. "But if it's a kiss that you're after, you're going to have to wait 'til the end of our date like a proper gentleman." Her quiet smile lit him up inside.

"You mean…? Really? Would you let me take you to dinner?" he rambled. "I'll get the money somehow. I'd sure like to spend some time with you."

She gave the dollar back to him. "Here, you keep this. And you come on over to my place tomorrow night and let me fix you some supper. How does that sound?" Together they stood, a wide grin spreading across his jaw.

"May I walk you home, Miss Lindsay?" he asked.

"I'd like that, thank you."

Daniel walked over to the nearby potted daisies that decorated the sidewalk and carefully looped his blue string around one of the stems, tying it in a clumsy bow.

Tomorrow I may not be here, but today I was.

La Petite Cathédrale D'elsie

Brien Crothers

Father Paolo gripped his cloak tight around his face, bent into the snowstorm, and moved on. A numb grip held his walking staff; fingers a mottled pink and pale, ghostly white. Aroused by the assault of another gust, he realized he no longer climbed with each step. Was this the vale he sought?

When the wind abated, snowflakes surrounding him held motionless, as if considering their mission toward earth. He caught the scent of burning wood. The snowflakes returned to their downward flutter. He stopped and turned toward the heartwarming aroma, a hound on the hunt, then started walking again. The day's light waned, and the temperature plummeted. Below his well-worn boots, the snow scrunched and squeaked. Paolo stopped and analyzed the smell of a villager's distant fire. He reoriented in its direction and stepped forward. Squeak, scrunch.

Though he felt certain of his path, he made slow progress.

Before him, a small structure loomed atop large beams. In the dark space below, a woman fed her cows. She stopped her work and turned toward the storm. She moved to the edge of her shelter and called out.

Father Paolo froze in place, not quite believing his dulled senses.

She called out again, and a cow lowed. And Paolo's world spun into darkness.

Woken by the woman's urging as she shook his shoulder, Father Paolo lay on his back, stunned, mouth agape. Through a dark haze, time spun backwards through his recent ordeal. He introduced himself and thanked God and the young woman.

His cloak hung on a peg near the rippling fire a few feet away, steam roiling from its sodden wool. Bits of ice lay on the floor below, thawing into thin puddles. Close to the fire, his boots sat, vapors lazily rising from their insides, looking as if they were two steeping cups of hot tea. The aroma of a savory meal drifted his way. This sent his mouth watering.

Beyond the crackling of the fire, Paolo heard the babbling of a child. He sat up—much too fast. His vision blurred. The woman caught him as he slumped toward the threadbare carpet lying beneath him. Senses returning, he looked into her eyes, then told her she had saved his life. She blushed and helped him to sit up, slower this time. He surveyed the room, with its low ceilings, dark log construction, and worn furniture. Amber light from a pair of candles and the fireplace danced across the humble scene.

The babbling resumed. Paolo twisted toward the sound. There, near a bed in one corner of the room, a cradle wobbled. He returned his gaze to the woman, and she nodded. With her help, Paolo stood. When his head had cleared, he took a few unsteady steps toward the cradle.

The woman said the baby's father had named her Elsie, after his grandmother.

The beautiful child's oval face, pink cheeks, and gleaming brown doe eyes lifted Paolo's spirits. The color of the child's rosy cheeks pulled at a memory from the padre's painful childhood; he pushed away the thought. The baby's mother beckoned him to sit at a small table, then placed a steaming bowl of stew before the priest. His stomach growled. He felt mortified by this ravenous response. She returned to the table with a bowl of her own and sat with Elsie on her lap. Father Paolo said a short blessing, then tucked into the thick, aromatic stew of braised meat, potatoes, carrots, and peas.

After Paolo's frenzied first bites, they spoke. He learned the woman's name was Luana, she was recently widowed, and that Elsie was five months old on this very day. The child watched Paolo's movements with delight and accepted portions of the stew's gravy from her mother's spoon. Elsie's eyes sparkled with the flicker of candle flames, her cheeks glowing red and reminding him of his twin sister, Revela, who had passed before their fourth birthday.

As the meal ended, Elsie cooed and reached out for him. With his smiling approval, her mother set Elsie on Paolo's lap. He had not held a child in years, but holding Elsie filled his heart. Father Paolo asked about the child's christening. Luana said their previous priest had to leave the village several weeks prior. Villagers waited for their new priest's arrival for christenings and weddings to take place. He looked from mother to child and back and declared a promise: because she had saved his life, he would christen her child before any other.

The next day woke to more gloom. Windows on one side of the woman's home were now half covered by snow. Icicles hung from the eves. The weather remained dreadful throughout that day. They heard loud snaps and sudden crashes, trees and their branches breaking from the burden of ice and snow. The bitter cold, blinding snowfall, and such hazards made it unsafe for any living beings outside their homes and dens. Paolo and his new friends spent the day by the fire.

The next morning the storm broke, and the sun rose in a low line over distant alpine peaks. As if from a cataclysm, villagers emerged from their homes. Cows lowed in their stalls.

Elsie's mother bundled her, and they guided an anxious Father Paolo to his new church. The old building stood two hundred yards away from the location of his deliverance from the fiendish snowstorm. Under a tall, snow-capped spire, the building sat with its hanging, bedraggled bands of faded paint. Paolo's heart sank at the sight of a house of God in such a deplorable state.

The young priest, using stiff leg muscles, pushed a thick snowdrift away from the entrance. That burdensome task completed, he shouldered the doors open and peered inside, the scene forbidding, cold and dark as an ice cave.

The village alderman presented himself. The older man, replete in a suit and tie under a long, fur-lined coat, informed Father Paolo someone would come to help light a fire in the boiler. Father Paolo informed the alderman that services would resume the next morning, Sunday.

With so little time before this first service, the boiler had done very little to ward off the chill in the church. In the sacristy, Father Paolo saw his breath. Nevertheless, nervous as a hare under a hawk's eye, he perspired under his cassock beneath liturgical vestments and silk stole. At the proper time, he stepped onto the dais and looked toward his congregation. In a space large enough for over one hundred people, sat less than two dozen. White puffs of breath mingled and held in a layer above the villagers.

During the days that proceeded the christening of baby Elsie, Father Paolo and the alderman's right-hand man, Alfred, fed wood into the boiler. It would take many more days before the heat would penetrate the thick walls of the church and bring comfort to its parishioners.

One Saturday evening two weeks later, as another storm dumped more snow in the valley, Father Paolo prepared for the next day's sermon and baby Elsie's christening. He set out his vestments and the silver cup and aspergil. Satisfied with his planning for the special event, he left the sacristy and walked across the dais, preparing to kneel at the altar.

Before Father Paolo could complete his prostration, Alfred burst through the doors of the church, gesticulating with both hands and bellowing incoherent sentences. Father Paolo, moved to panic by the sudden frenzy, calmed himself, settled the man into a mid-row pew, and asked him to repeat his message.

Word had come that Luana and her child had not returned from her mother-in-law's home, well above the village near the Col de la Forclaz. Alfred also declared that this new blizzard had blown in as heavy as the last.

Alfred, fearful, sat with hands clutched in his lap and his head down. He informed the priest that the men of the village were on their way; they would begin their search for mother and child from the church.

Village men stomped into the church, thick wads of snow falling from coats and shaken from their hats. The unorganized herd clamored for several minutes, each of the men speaking over the others. Father Paolo was at a loss. As if on cue, the alderman entered, surveyed the scene, and said a few words. The men quickly organized their search. Father Paolo said a quick prayer, and the men, now roped together in pairs and trios, set off into the dusk, lanterns in hand.

As the snow continued its cascade from the heavens, Father Paolo asked God for advice. Nothing came. He asked where his newest friends could be. No answer. He was preparing another query when several of the village women spilled into the church, all talking at once and beckoning for the priest. Another flood of snow fell to the wooden floors. Someone rushed off for a pail and mop. With Father Paolo's agreement, the women set up narrow tables and laid out warm food and hot beverages for the men's return. Father Paolo offered a prayer and asked God his next question. What more could they do? Still no divine reply. The women returned to their tasks.

Paolo kneeled before the effigy of Christ and asked what his Lord meant for him to learn from this experience. Only silence. Paolo remained still for long moments. Suddenly, a warm feeling blanketed him, God's meaning filling him. The angelic faces of baby Elsie and of Paolo's dearly departed sister Revela, each smiling their assent, filled his mind's eye.

He stood; hope was not lost. Returning to the women, he made a declaration: If right then they could make plans to paint the old church the following spring, bringing all the people together in that task, he believed that the village would be blessed, and mother and child would soon return.

The women discussed the idea amongst themselves. Paolo paced.

Moments later, the women paired up and set out into the storm to visit nearby village homes. Within an hour's time, they piled buckets with remnants of various colored paints in a corner of the church opposite the baptismal font. The ladies told Father Paolo this was all the paint in the village of Trient, and that it may not be enough for all of the church. He thought of the up-valley homes, their spare bits of paint. There must be more. The priest said God would understand and with His blessings they would find more paint before spring.

Tense minutes, then hours, passed; the old building fell into a worried silence. The ladies' hushed voices faded away from the priest's awareness. Father Paolo, deep in contemplation, walked the long aisle, past the transept, and returned to the altar. He kneeled once more and murmured his words to God, telling of the villagers' 'valiant efforts. On both knees, hands clasped tightly before him, he slid through his life, hovering over his rescue from the previous blizzard and when he had first met the radiant child, Elsie, and her fearless mother, now struggling to survive somewhere out there in the dark.

He started a different prayer, this time louder, his voice bouncing off the angular walls of the apse and the stained-glass images of saints in tall windows above. Before he could finish his appeal, a clamor broke the silence. The doors of the church burst open, and a throng of men poured into the main aisle, encircling a bundled figure holding a smaller bundle. More men, and then more, entered. The swirling mix of bodies overflowed into the pews. From the bundled figure appeared Luana. She undid a fleece that had protected her child from the cold; Elsie's tiny smile and rosy cheeks beamed. They all cheered with delight. Father Paolo turned back and thanked God and Jesus in a long prayer. Tears streamed down his face for the first time in his adult life.

Next morning, the storm now abated, baby Elsie and mother arrived at the church first. Then a dozen villagers appeared, and a dozen more.

Beyond the sacristy walls, Father Paolo could hear a din rising up in the nave. The thought of Elsie and her mother waiting for him lifted his body. He donned his garments, clutched his Bible to his chest and made for the door. From the altar, Father Paolo looked up. The first set of pews were full, Elsie and her mother beside the aisle. Villagers crammed into the second set. As he continued his survey, expectant faces filled every pew. Others stood in the back and along the walls.

Mass complete, Father Paolo announced Elsie's christening. A cheer rose from the crowd. The priest led Luana and Elsie through the now standing, expectant people to the baptismal font. Elsie wore a long christening gown. Generations of use proudly shown as an off-white hue in the garment's delicate fabric. Elsie gabbed and cooed to everyone's delight.

Somewhat nervous, Father Paolo said the words of his faith and sprinkled holy water from the aspergil. The christening complete, Luana dried the baby's fine, light hair and bundled her up once more. Festivities over, they all filed out into the daylight, each taking the time to address mother and daughter as they passed.

When the following spring arrived, the people found more paint on long forgotten shelves and in cellars throughout the valley. Father Paolo organized a ceremony to mix all the paints following Sunday church services. To begin their undertaking, the alderman recalled the horrific storms of the past winter and their dire circumstances. He then asked Father Paolo to give thanks.

Preambles concluded, villagers began opening pails, pouring their contents into a large barrel, and mixing the various paints together.

Two large men standing over the barrel and using willow branches stirred the thick goo with all their might. Elsie's mother held her close to the proceedings. She chattered and attempted various words. In the barrel, thin swirls and traces of the various pigments mixed in a colorful spiraling mosaic. Nearby villagers predicted that the result would be a boring brown or a dull gray. As the new color materialized, the people crowded close. Each would look into the barrel, then to Elsie, then to each other, and then cross themselves.

Father Paolo noticed the people's response and looked into the barrel. He too looked to Elsie. He softly caressed her tiny cheeks. Those close by smiled in delight. Father Paolo declared to those who could not see for the crowd that little Elsie had inspired the color their church would become. To everyone's amazement, the new creation was a perfect match for the child's rosy, pink cheeks.

That springtime in Trient, so many years ago, Father Paolo had warned the villagers their church would likely never house a bishop's cathedra. However, ever since, they have called their church La Petite Cathédrale d'Elsie—Elsie's little cathedral.

Zahir And Nobody

Geoffrey K. Leigh

The man lives in the same small village where he was born. He works as a carpenter his whole life, and he enjoys both his profession and his hometown. But Zahir no longer experiences fulfillment from his work. He senses there must be more to life. Yet, he doesn't know quite what he's missing. Not long after becoming aware of his yearning for more contentment, he finds himself in a neighboring town. He goes there to deliver a beautiful wooden bowl he made specifically for his friend, who lives there. As they sit and drink tea following the examination of the carving, Zahir shares his desire to find more meaning in his life.

His friend looks at him for a moment, then replies, "I suggest you go visit the man who lives in the mountain cave. Just follow this road up the hill. You'll see the door on your right near the top."

"Why? What does he do?"

"Do? He grows food nearby or sits and talks to people. I just think you might find a visit fruitful." Trusting his friend, Zahir decides to talk with the man. "What's his name?" he asks. "How will I know him?" "His name? Nobody. And he's the only one who lives in that area. You'll find him."

Zahir thanks his friend, packs the money for the bowl into the rucksack, and begins his trek up the mountain. Because Zahir walks everywhere, he finds the hike only moderately strenuous. The white and purple flowers along the road brighten his walk. Their scent entices him as the sun warms his back1. Zahir stops and bends down to smell the wildflowers. He begins to wonder if he should take a gift to the man, as he forgot to ask his friend if that were customary. His rucksack contains nothing other than money and some food. So, he decides to pick a bouquet, in case that would be a thoughtful gesture when he meets the man.

As he approaches the summit, Zahir begins to look for the cave. Yet, this three-hour walk enervated his body. Finally, he spots an entrance into the hill where a man sits on a stool with eyes shut, his back against a rock surrounding the opening. The man's hair and beard blend with the white granite. He wears a brown robe and sandals. As Zahir approaches him, the man, without opening his eyes, says, "Hi. Welcome to my home. Would you like to sit down for a while?"

"Yes, I would. Thank you, sir. It's a long walk here. Are you Mr. Nobody?"

"Yes, I am Nobody," the man says as he opens his eyes. "And what did you contemplate about as you walked here?"

"Well, I wondered if you would like some flowers?"

"Yes, I'd love them. They have a sweet flavor, especially the purple ones. Do you have other items you would share?"

"I just sold a lovely bowl. I have some money."

"I can't eat money. Do you have anything else?"

"I have some bread and honey."

"Would you mind sharing half with me?"

"I'd be happy to, sir." Zahir pulls out his bread and breaks it in half, as Nobody goes into his cave. He comes out with a gray jar chiseled from stone and hands it to Zahir, who pours half his honey into it. Nobody smells the sweetness, puts the lid on it, and takes it and the bread inside. Then he returns and sits down on his padded stool. "What brings you to my home today, Zahir?" 52

Zahir's mouth gapes open. "How did you know my name?"

"It was written on the side of the honey bottle," Nobody chuckles.

"Oh, of course," responds Zahir, joining in the laughter. "Well, I've been thinking there must be more to life than making things, eating, and sleeping. While I love to create carvings out of beautiful objects from nature, it feels like I'm missing something in life. My wife has died, and my two children moved to the city for work. Now I feel little meaning in living."

"Did you mourn your wife's death?"

"Oh yes, for many years. It feels like my eyes have run dry."

"Then it is time to expand your chest and develop new tears. For they are the watering system of the heart."

"My wife was a big heart opener. I'm not sure I know how to expand it any longer."

"How much do you want to open your heart now?"

"As if my life depends on it."

"Good. Because it does." With that, Nobody reaches out with both hands and touches the visitor's chest. Zahir feels a formidable zap, then he falls off the rock onto his side. There he remains for an extended time. He slowly wakes, pulls back the blanket that now covers him, and looks up to see Nobody sitting on his stool eating bread and honey. Zahir pushes against the ground to raise himself, then slides back onto the rock. "Wow, I think I must have dozed off. How long was I out?"

"Two days," responds Nobody.

"What? No! That's not possible. I thought it was an hour or so."

"No, just about two full days. Want something to eat?"

"Yes, I'm starved." Nobody goes into his cave, returning with some spiced cooked grain and beans along with a cup of water. The mixture stimulates Zahir's hunger even further. He gobbles down the food, followed by several gulps of liquid. "My heart feels so full. What did you do?"

"Oh, I just helped you along with your wish. I suggest you go back home and continue your work. When you start to feel your heart close down, give something to someone who needs it. Or tell someone what you appreciate about them. And take this heart-shaped rock with you to remind you of your intention."

"May I give you some money?" asks Zahir.

"No, just keep living from your heart. That's the best gift you can give me."

Zahir thanks Nobody and walks back down the mountain, stopping in his friend's village to thank him.

"Did he help you?" his friend asks.

"Oh yes. He's probably the second greatest gift in my life."

"Fabulous. I'm glad he was helpful," replies his friend, rather sure Zahir's deceased wife remains his greatest gift, at least until now.

Zahir walks back to his village. Once at home, he continues his carving, which becomes more creative and stunning. People come from extended regions of the country, hearing about his extraordinary creations, the beauty of the wood or stone, and the velvet feel of the surfaces. Some are stone or wooden animals, others carved people, or scenes from the area.

But as Zahir continues the expansive opening of his chest, the trunk of his body increasingly morphs into a heart shape. As that transpires, the villagers' aversion to him proliferates. They begin to shun him. It becomes increasingly difficult for him to get food, clothes, or other needed supplies.

Zahir decides to move away. He packs up his belongings and carving tools, sells his house, and moves to a distant part of the country, everything he owns stuffed into his cart. The rock Nobody passed on to him gets carefully tucked into his rucksack. He also begins to wear colorful oversized cloaks, hiding his body so others won't be scared.

In his new village, Zahir finds a house with a shop in front where he can display his work. He can live in back with a small window to watch the shop and a back door to enter or leave his home. He displays the wooden and stone carvings he makes in the shop with a price sign by each. As people enter, a bell rings, and Zahir, donning his large cloak, comes out to help them. Hiding his body makes it easier for others to interact with him.

As people examine his exotic carvings, they increasingly enter into conversation with Zahir. Customers begin to spend greater amounts of time chatting with him rather than solely focusing on the carvings. Later, as more people gather in the shop, Zahir brings out his carved stools or elegant pillows for people to sit on as they prolong their discussions. Visitors often ask him for advice about their lives or how they might solve differences with their spouse, friends, and neighbors.

"I don't really know anything about all that. I just know about the heart. If you take what people say personally, you sensitize the organ to collect pain. This is not feeling the pain of others, but rather internalizing the hurt they pass on to you. As people fling cruel words your way, both your hearts live in contracted pain. Yet, the heart is naturally strong when we don't make it small. If you don't sensitize it to take on pain from other's words, then it can hold tremendous grief and gigantic love. It is built for strength and longevity. But when we constrict it by taking on the pain and hurt passed to us by others, our heart has a more difficult time."

"So how do we avoid taking on such pain? How do we strengthen the heart?" one neighbor asks.

"First, by recognizing that others' hurtful words are not about you, but about them. So don't make the pain yours. Allow the words to fly through without becoming attached to them. Second, you open the heart through gratitude. Share appreciations with your spouse, your children, your friends. Feel gratitude for the beauty of this land or for some small gift you've received. Grieve fully for a loss or for the pain that exists in the lives of those around you. Then give joy when the grief is fully expressed, once gratitude and love have returned."

The crowds grow when the rain stops. Zahir and the villagers move to the hillside behind his home, as the shop no longer can contain such large groups. The fresh air relaxes them, and they relish the scent of honeysuckle and jasmine on the hill. When the sun comes out, Zahir's cloak gets hotter. First, he removes the hood, and people continue their conversations. When he stands up to make a point and the cloak falls open, not a sound occurs. People keep listening and asking questions.

Finally, one woman in the front raises her hand, and Zahir nods for her to speak. "I see your heart is so open that it has influenced your body. Could you help us do that, Mr. Heartman? I want my heart to be that big."

Zahir stands still in shock, both at the ease of her question about his visible body shape and her reference to a new name. "Well, I suppose I could, although I'm not exactly sure how this happened. But I will help all I can."

People continue to come, sometimes different guests on different days. Many stop in the shop to buy a stool or pillow for sitting on the hill, or a creation because of its beauty. Since Zahir spends little time attending to his carvings, he puts a sign in front. It reads:

The attendant is not available.

Please take a carving you like and leave a little money in its place.

Thank you. The Management.

Zahir enjoys meal preparation, but little time exists most days for that, too. The villagers now bring food to share with him and each other. As people spend greater time around him, they find themselves happier, more relaxed, more concerned with others, and even healing their own illnesses in some cases. So, they want more opportunities in group conversations and in Zahir's presence.

One day, a man raises his hand. "How do we help our children open their hearts?" he asks. "Oh, you don't have to worry about teaching children to open their hearts," responds Zahir. "What you pay attention to is avoiding words and behaviors that encourage them to close down their hearts, like most adults already have done."

Another man stands, and Zahir motions for him to speak. "As I focus more on my heart, my wife says my sexual desire has decreased dramatically. While she likes my greater openness, she is not happy about my lack of physical interest. What do you recommend?"

Zahir looks into the man, closes his eyes, and remains on his stool for a few moments. The crowd watches him in silence. After a time, he opens his eyes and speaks. "Is your wife here with you?" he asks.

"No, she stayed home to prepare more food. She'll be here tomorrow while I stay home to work."

"I suggest you go home, take your wife into your bedroom and remove all clothes. Sit in a comfortable place and take turns telling each other ways that you are grateful for your spouse, at least 10 times each. Afterwards, give each other a big hug. Then allow yourselves to roll around on the floor laughing, loving, kissing, and touching each other. Ask her to report back tomorrow. I suggest you go begin immediately."

The man gets up, thanks Zahir, and leaves.

The next day, a woman in front raises her hand as soon as Zahir welcomes the crowd. He motions for her to share. "Yesterday, you gave my husband some instructions about our physical connection. I just want to say we had the best sex ever. Thank you!"

"I see," says Zahir. "Could you speculate about why that might have been?"

"I don't know for sure, and who knows if it will work every time. But my guess is that when both our hearts and bodies are open to each other, our physical and energetic connections are greatly amplified. I think my husband got so focused on opening his heart that he left his body behind," laughs his wife. "But I think we are finding our way back to verbally and physically expressing our love."

The crowd applauds at the wife's remarks. Zahir joins the response.

Over time, the size and frequency of gatherings decrease. Instead, spontaneous conversations and exchanges of gratitude take place all over the village. As such discussions increase, body shapes begin to replicate their hearts. Now Zahir appears normal among his community. He quits wearing cloaks and begins to create heart-designed

clothing in bright and lively colors, exaggerating rather than conceal-
ing the new body shapes.

Some people come to town and become afraid of the strange-
looking residents, disappearing as quickly as they arrive. Others visit
and notice how happily and peacefully the people live. Some relocate
to the village, wanting to participate in this intriguing community.

Zahir feels sadness that he can't touch the hearts of people who
don't remain. It seems to him their fear of what they see overpowers
the subtle access to love. So, he spends time at the edge of town,
giving hugs to all who want, softening defenses and touching their
hearts without conditions, as he receives.

Night School Outing

Penelope Anne Cole

"Tell me what you see?" Tom pointed to one of the old windows, eye level for him.

Street lights don't illuminate much here in the now deserted warehouse district—and no help from the misting rain. *But nighttime is the best time for sleuthing, right?* I thought.

All of five foot one, I peeked in on tiptoe, helped by an old brick I placed against the wall. I shone my Maglite around. "There's nobody here."

Tom shook his straggly, gray head, gave a disgusted snort, then wiped rain off his glasses.

"Tell me everything—every single thing you see." He put his glasses back on and glared at me.

I shrank some—his disdain bruised my spirit. *See more or face more criticism.* I strained up and peered inside again. My uneven breathing stirred dust particles untouched by the drizzle into my nose. Not allowing a sneeze, I wiped it on my damp sleeve. My intense gaze followed the beam around the room.

"It's a huge warehouse, empty except for two old chairs facing each other with a crate beside them. I see footsteps in the dust around both chairs and drag marks where the crate, and maybe something else, was moved."

"That's a bit better. Detectives have to observe more, see every-thing. We look for evidence, clues. Was somebody here? Alone or with someone else? What did they do here? Then we put all the obser-vations together."

Tom shrugged his shoulders. He reached inside his jacket but scowled, when apparently, he didn't find his trademark cigarettes. Instead, he pulled out a worn pipe and chewed on the stem.

"These kids," he muttered, "looking for the easy way, the fast track." He brushed rain off his tweed jacket—seemingly a gesture of dismissal.

Heat rose from my neck up to my overlong bangs. No shrinking now, as I whirled to face him.

"I chose this class to learn from the best—you. But you lump us all together as kids—demeaning us to puff yourself up." I'd hurled the words at him, then instantly regretted my bravado. *Uh oh, I've done it now—what must he think of me?*

Tom's mouth gaped at my onslaught. But before he could respond, I finished my truth telling.

"And I'm no kid. I'm nearly thirty with a nine-year-old. I need to work. It's not *easy* that I want, but to get good." I pushed my wet bangs back from my forehead, as I blew out my breath. My defiance fading, I shook and readjusted my wet hat.

"Then show me you've got what it takes. At least you've got some spunk. Not like the other kids—note-taking and nodding like fools. If you really want this, you'll have to work harder than you've ever worked before. They don't hire timid, sloppy PIs. Clients must have confidence in you, so you need to believe in and prove yourself."

Tom stepped around to the back of the building, obviously searching for something. He stopped in front of a banged-up dumpster. He looked it over and grinned his satisfaction.

"What about this here? Could it tell you something?" Tom patted the side of the wet dumpster like it was a special delivery package. "You want more information, here it is."

I wasn't about to disappoint him again, but the idea of looking in a dumpster grossed me out. *Does he want me to climb inside?* I nearly gagged at the thought, but gritted my teeth. *If this is another test, I won't fail.*

I spotted a discarded shipping pallet and drug it over to the dumpster. Then I climbed on top of it, slid the bar to unlock it, and heaved the wet steel lid open. My flashlight at the ready—*here goes nothing.* I mentally divided the interior into grids and systematically moved the beam from grid to grid. *So far, just garbage.* Then I gasped when I saw something that froze my blood.

"There's clothing in here, but it's not limp, like discards or rags. It's covering something. I need a closer look." I pulled on my latex evidence gloves and wished I had my elbow length garden gloves. The dumpster was full of garbage, not just trash, but things wet from the rain and other fluids. I gingerly lifted a corner of the clothing. It was covering a shoulder! I expelled a ragged breath. Tom couldn't see what I saw, but he probably noticed the stiffness of my back and knew from my gasp that I'd found more than we'd expected.

Tom's voice roared above the whooshing sounds of the rain pouring down the gutter. "What *is* it, kid? Tell me what you see."

I ignored the kid label, turned toward him, my face lacking much feeling now. "It's a shoulder. Someone's in the dumpster."

I was glad to get down when he grabbed my arm and pulled me off the pallet to take my place. With his height, Tom could reach further than I could. He tugged on the jacket, moving the shoulder a little. I heard a weak moan.

"Call 911," Tom barked. His urgency compelled me.

I fumbled for my mobile phone in my wet back pocket. I pushed numbers as fast as my shaking, gloved hands allowed. I knew from class that we shouldn't move anything and possibly destroy evidence. But I was also sure the guy wasn't comfortable in his metal coffin, hearing the drumming rainfall. Tom gently cleared some of the garbage away to give the person breathing room, all the while speaking in an unexpected, soothing voice.

"It's okay, son, help is on the way. Can you speak? Can you move your arms? Legs? Don't move if it hurts anywhere—something might be broken."

Another moan, louder this time. Then sirens in the distance. *Help is coming.* They got reassuringly louder. The moaning became weak sobbing.

The boy must've thought he was a goner. And he would have been if Tom hadn't arranged this nighttime field trip. I wonder, did Tom have a sixth sense that made him pick that dumpster? And why did this happen on my turn? Just my luck. I have more questions for Tom— once the kid's safely in the ambulance.

I breathed deeply of the rain-freshened air and waved the medics in closer, with the police car following behind them.

"We'll have to give our statements to the police, obviously," Tom said to me, but he didn't leave the boy's side.

It's going to be an even longer night now. Glad my Sophie is at Gram's—some normalcy on this bizarre night school outing. Glad the kid's alive. Heck, I guess I'm glad it was my turn after all.

*   *   *

After the police took our statements and the ambulance rushed the teen to the hospital, Tom turned to me, nodding his head.

"You did okay, kid. Actually, not bad for your first time out. We'll talk about this more in Monday's class. Probably best you head home now. And write up your notes while it's still fresh."

"Okay. See you Tuesday night." *Monday is a holiday, as indicated below. There wouldn't be a class on a holiday?* It looked like he was going to say more, as he leaned toward me, but he just smiled. *Was he going to pat me? Like I'm a good girl. I winced at that thought. Maybe he's not used to "girls" doing okay.*

We walked to our cars. He opened the door to his Land Rover, which looked like it was an Army reject. I slid into my battered sub-compact, all I could afford on my waitress pay. I waved and started backing out. Then I saw Tom reach into his vehicle, pull out a camera with a telescopic lens, and a satchel—maybe his notebook. As I drove off, I saw him shine his Maglite along the driveway, and it lingered on the warehouse doors. Then he headed over to the side window where I'd peeked in. *Maybe he's gone to get some pictures to show me what I missed,* I harrumphed to myself. *Should I stay with him? But he hadn't said I needed to. So, I'm off to Gram's to pick up Sophie.*

As I drove through silent rain-slicked streets, I reviewed everything we'd seen. I ticked each thing off in order to organize my thoughts for my notes. Then decided to record it on my phone.

After our last class, it was to be my turn to practice sleuthing skills. Tom had told us to use all our senses. What did we see, hear, smell, touch, feel, intuit? Was anything amiss or did something seem not quite right? For me, he'd picked a warehouse in the nearly abandoned industrial sector of the city. We'd gotten there shortly after dark.

"We'll be looking for anything, noting if something appears to be out of the ordinary, or seems out of place."

Naturally, with my luck, it was a rainy night. It couldn't be nice and clear with a full moon. Nope, dark and cloudy with intermittent rainfall, a slight breeze to blow the rain and drizzle around, making it harder to see. I'd brought my Maglite, as instructed. By the time we got there, it was drizzling steadily, so I was glad for my all-weather shoes and rain jacket.

After we'd parked, Tom told me I was on my own. I walked to the locked double warehouse doors. It didn't look like they'd been opened recently. I didn't see any obvious tire tracks, but it was gravel, so I'm not sure what I would have seen even in daylight. Then I noticed the side windows and walked over there to take a peek. But he'd wanted me to do more investigating, so he picked that dumpster for me to "look into". Then we'd found the kid, well, the teen, half buried in the dumpster. But why was he there at night? He wasn't dressed for the evening chill or the rainy weather. How long had he been there?

My heart went out to the poor guy. Left alone, likely to die, since it was a Friday night and there'd not be any business going on until Monday. No, Monday's a holiday, so maybe not until Tuesday. Could the teen have lasted three days in the dumpster? It was supposed to get hotter on Saturday and Sunday. How could he survive in that metal box once it got to the 90s? Oh my God—they left him alone to die! That realization hit me so hard, I almost stomped on the brakes.

At Gram's house, I parked and rushed inside. She was in the kitchen with her hands on her hips and a frown on her face. *Oh, she's going to be even more unhappy with me in a minute.*

"Well, it's about time you waltzed in here. Did you forget I was just to watch Sophie for a couple of hours on your field trip? Here, I've made you a sandwich and you can sleep on the sofa tonight. You're not going to wake Sophie up at this time of night." Gram gestured to the table and started to get me the sandwich.

"No time, Gram. I just came in to tell you I've got to go to the hospital." I told her the barest bones' version of the outing, as I hugged her, grabbed my laptop, and strode to the front door.

"I'll tell you more tomorrow. Sorry to stick you with Sophie for Saturday, but I'm sure she'll be fine. Thanks much." Gram nodded and shoved the sandwich in my bag.

I ate the sandwich as I drove to the hospital. The teen must have seen something that put his life in danger. And as soon as he was able, he'd give his statement to the police, and I wanted to be there for that. What had he seen that threatened his life? *No one should be left alone to die. I'll be there when he wakes up.*

At the hospital front desk, there was Tom, beaming at me. "So, you figured it out, did you?" He crowed.

"I know he saw something that he shouldn't have, so they left him to die. The dumpster was shut up from the outside before a three-day weekend. But no one should be left all alone. So, I'm here for him when he wakes up."

"Right, and we'll find out more and maybe piece it together. I called a captain friend of mine at the Station. He said the kid hadn't told them anything, not that the doctor would let her patient be grilled. He's got a broken arm, severe bruising all over like from being punched or kicked, and he was badly dehydrated. So likely he'd been in the dumpster longer than just today when we found him."

"I didn't know you could get patient information like that. Isn't it private?"

"Yeah, but the doctor is my ex. She'd not let me interrogate any of her patients, but she disclosed his condition when I told her how I found him and I was investigating the case."

"You mean how *I* found him," I bristled. "Investigating the case?"

"Captain Townsend said he'd appreciate my expertise since *WE* found the boy. You saw me hang back at the warehouse, right? I knew there hadn't been any real business at that warehouse for months, maybe even years. So, there was no reason for the brand-new lock on the double doors. No reason for the chairs, crate, and dust to be disturbed like you saw. And no reason for anything to be in the dumpster, let alone a kid, locked in. I expect all that in your write up. So, yes, I'll be here when he wakes up. You can stay or go." He parked himself in the waiting room, stretched out, pulled his hat over his face, and dozed off.

I settled next to him, pulled out my laptop, and started typing. *Yep, it really was a long night, and getting longer, on to morning, when we'll get some answers on our case.*

Ronnie's Surprise Gift

Geoffrey K. Leigh

"**D**on't leave your bike in the driveway. Your Mom may not see it when she backs out and could wreck it!" shouts Lance, Ronnie's father and church pastor. "You need to take better care of your possessions, or you won't have anything to play with. Money doesn't just magically appear, young man," reminds his dad for the millionth time as he returns to the house.

Ronnie walks over and moves his bike the necessary seven inches to get it off the driveway. Then he goes back to his basketball game where he's beating the national championship team. Even when he misses layups or jump shots, he manages to get the rebound and shoot again. He's warm still, during an uncommon heat wave occurring this early winter. And Ronnie wants to finish what may be his last game of the year. As he makes his shot, Stevie and Mikey, his two younger brothers, emerge from the open garage.

"We wanna play too. How about four horses?" asks Stevie.

"In a few minutes," responds Ronnie. "I'm almost finished with my championship game."

"What game? You're playing all by yourself," says Stevie.

"No, it's a game. You just can't see the other players."

Stevie and Mikey stand there with their mouths gapping open. Mikey, age 5, squints to see who else might be there, just in case his oldest brother is being serious.

Ronnie makes the winning basket and begins to cheer. His father comes out of the garage and tells them to get into the house to take baths. "You need to be clean for church tomorrow."

"But dad, I don't want to go. Besides, we're starting our final game with good weather."

Lance walks over and slaps Ronnie across the face. "Don't you ever say that about church again. Jesus is the most important person in our lives, and church is the place we learn to love and obey him. Once you are Born Again, you'll know these things and receive salvation." He grabs Stevie and Mikey by their arms and jerks them towards him. "And don't you two start acting stupid like your brother, if you want Jesus to love you!"

The three boys walk towards the house, heads down, faces sullen, with Lance following on Ronnie's heels. Once inside, the boys go upstairs to their bedrooms, hearing water running into the tub.

"Tilly will be out shortly," says Millie, their mother. "But don't go far. You need to get in there and get all clean for Jesus. Kimie's already finished, so you'll be next."

The boys go into their rooms looking for jammies to put on after their bath. Ronnie lies down on his bed to read until his turn. He thinks about church and how much he dislikes it, sitting there so long while the congregation sings, his dad preaches, more singing, more preaching. And Ronnie tries to ignore it all. He enjoys the last part when everyone cheers Hallelujah. Then the whole church thing is over.

"KIMIE, CALL 9-1-1, NOW!" shouts Millie. "Tell them we need an ambulance at this address."

Ronnie jumps off his bed and rushes down. "What's the matter, Mom?"

"There's something wrong with your dad. Go outside and show in the medics!"

Millie kneels by Lance, as he groans and holds his left arm, rolling around on the floor. Ronnie stares at his dad's flushed face, then goes outside. He looks up and down the street, anxiously awaiting any approaching vehicle with a reassuring siren. Once the ambulance arrives, a man and woman jump out, grab the stretcher out of the back, then follow Ronnie, who's running towards the house.

The man talks with Millie and asks all sorts of questions, while the woman kneels next to Lance, checking his heart, pulse, and breathing. Once examined, they carefully put Ronnie's dad on the stretcher, roll him outside, and place him in the back of the vehicle while Millie and the family follow.

"OK, we'll call ahead. You get there as quickly as you can, safely. He'll be in the emergency area," says the woman sitting next to Lance as the man heads for the driver's door. With siren at full blast, the ambulance rushes away.

"Kimie, glad you're here. You watch the kids. I'm going to the hospital. I'll call you as soon as I know anything. No use all of us being there with nothing but impatience."

"Mom, I want to go too," says Ronnie. "Maybe I can help you with something."

"OK, Ronnie. But we need to go now."

They both dash to the garage. Ronnie pushes the door button, then gets into the van. Millie backs out, shifts gears, and rushes towards the hospital, her head remaining straightforward, her eyes filling with moisture.

"He'll be OK, Mom. I'm sure. He's not that old, and he's strong," says Ronnie pleadingly.

Millie looks at him, tears streaming down her cheeks. "Thanks, Ronnie. Glad you're here." Relief fills Ronnie sitting next to Mom, despite the mixed feelings he has about his father.

"There's a space close to the entrance," says Ronnie. Millie pulls in quickly. Ronnie knows it isn't a good time to say anything, but inside he smiles about this race car side of Mom, never having seen her drive so fast. They scurry into the Emergency Room, then spot the information counter.

"We're here to see Lance Hardas, please. The ambulance would've brought him in a few minutes ago."

"Ah, yes. He's in with the emergency doctor now. Just take a seat, and I'll point you out when the doctor's free."

Millie and Ronnie find two seats by themselves in the intimate waiting area with silence and the scent of disinfectant as their companions. A woman in the corner attempts to console her child. Millie grabs Ronnie's hand as the tissue in her other hand wipes the moisture from her face.

"Really Mom, I think he's gonna be OK." Ronnie leans his head onto his Mom's shoulder, pretending to care about dad, and the two sit there for some time. Millie picks up a *Vogue* and stares at the cover, never opening the magazine.

"Excuse me, Mrs. Hardas?" Millie and Ronnie look up to see a tall, thin woman with dark hair and intense eyes, in a white lab coat, a stethoscope draped around her neck. "Are you Mrs. Hardas?"

"Yes, I am."

"Hi. I'm Dr. Simpkins. Your husband's doing pretty well. But he's had a serious heart attack caused by a blockage in the left anterior descending artery. This can be very dangerous, and I think he should undergo an operation immediately. Time is of the essence with such blockages. I'd like you to talk with the nurse at the window and take care of the paperwork. With your permission, I'm going back in to prep your husband for surgery."

Millie's eyes water again. "Yes . . . um . . . of course! I'll go see the nurse right now. Will he be alright?"

"There's a good chance, given that we got him here so quickly, and he seems healthy otherwise. The EKG confirms our suspicion. So, we need to get him in right away. Unless there are any questions, I'll talk with you immediately after surgery."

"No. Please, do what you think's best," replies Millie softly.

With that, the doctor disappears behind the swinging doors.

After completing the paperwork, Millie returns to her seat and takes out her phone. She calls Kimie to let her know what's happening and that they won't be home anytime soon. Kimie sounds calm, her voice flat. Ronnie sympathizes with her, sharing her anger about their "Jesus- loving, heavy- handed" father. Kimie, the oldest child, and Ronnie, the oldest son, seem to get the brunt of their father's fury. Now Ronnie's with his Mom, where he feels safest. But he also worries that Jesus will punish him because he lacks sincere love for his dad, with more guilt than concern about surviving the surgery.

Ronnie reads several articles in the available *Sports Illustrated*, sleeps until his neck hurts, then watches his mother doze intermittently. Finally, Ronnie softly nudges his Mom when the doctor returns. She opens her eyes and sits up straight.

"So, we're finished with the surgery, and your husband did well. It was a little touch and go for a short time. But he seems to be resting now, and his vitals are stable. We'll want to keep him here for a few more days. It's getting rather late, and I suspect he'll sleep the remainder of the night from the meds. I suggest you go home, get some sleep yourselves, and come back to see him in the morning."

"Thank you so much, Dr. Simpkins. We really appreciate all you've done for him."

"You're very welcome. I'm just happy we got to him early."

Millie takes Ronnie's hand as they go outside, locate the van and drive home, apparently without the race car Mom. Upon arrival, they find the house quiet and dark. Ronnie goes into the kitchen, searching for food. Millie follows and pulls out some leftovers, heats them up, and the two sit down for a late snack. Ronnie's too tired for conversation. Upon finishing, he gets up, puts his dishes in the sink, and walks back to his mom.

"Told you he was going to be OK, Mom. I'll see you in the morning."

"Love you, Ronnie. Thanks for being with me tonight."

"Sure, Mom. Love you too!" Ronnie leans in, and they hug each other.

The next few days are busy, as the family visits Lance and cleans up the house for his return. After his dad gets home, Ronnie notices a quieter and softer man. But Ronnie figures the "preacher" is just recovering his strength and will show up again any time now.

Several days after leaving the hospital, Lance and Millie have a chance to talk while the kids are in school. Lance breaks the silence. "I had an astonishing experience while in surgery."

"What happened, dear?"

"Well, I found myself hovering over the operating table. Then I saw this tunnel of light off to my right, and I followed it. It felt really good as I moved upwards. When I emerged from it, there was a man who had long dark hair, a dark beard, and was dressed in white with a bright glow about him. I was shocked.

"Then he told me, 'It's not your time yet. You have work to do, and your family needs you.' I asked him, 'What do I need to do?' As he looked at me, love flowed from his eyes and he said, 'People need to know the truth. You focus on a Supreme Being primarily about rules and punishment. But what about love? Do you feel that?' he asked. I could feel this overwhelming affection and acceptance that was all around and inside my body. 'Yes,' I said. 'What is that?' He looked at me and smiled, 'That's who you are. That's what you are made of and your gift to each other when you're in touch with it and share it. Love doesn't just originate in the Divine or someone else. It's the core of each of us. I want you to go back and share this message with your family and your congregation. But not just with your words. Show it by how you live your life, treat other people, and respect the earth.' I couldn't believe that after studying the Scriptures in seminary, I'd never really heard or focused on such a message. But it also was difficult to return, to leave the unconditional love I felt."

"Wow, that's incredible. What are you going to do?" asks Millie, her eyes tearing up.

"I don't know. But I know I can't keep living and preaching the way I've been doing."

During the next few days, family members notice not only Lance's slower pace, but also his softer voice and manner. Others start to observe a difference, too. In church that next Sunday, the assistant pastor gives a sermon on compassion. Lance talks with him after and compliments him on his remarks rather than criticizing something he did wrong or missed, as he typically did in the past. The minister stares at him for a moment, mouth half open, then thanks him.

As they walk out of the church, Lance takes Millie's hand for the first time Ronnie ever remembers. He points this out to Kimie, who gives him an odd look. They shrug their shoulders, then climb into the van.

Later in the week, the family makes preparations for Ronnie's birthday. Presents get wrapped and put out on a table. With the food on the table, everyone sits down for the dinner Millie prepared at Ronnie's request.

During the meal, Lance asks, "Why can't kids remember past birthdays?"

Everyone looks at Lance with shock. Ronnie never remembers him ever attempting to tell a joke. Stevie finally replies, "I don't know, why Daddy?"

"Because they're too focused on the present." Lance begins to laugh, as do Mikey, Stevie and Tilly. Millie, Kimie, and Ronnie look at him in wonderment. Eventually, they all laugh, as much at the kids as the joke.

That night, Stevie brings Lance the Bible as they gather for the birthday celebration. Instead of his usual birthday passage, Lance opens the book to a different section and begins to read.

"Love one another as I have loved you. I'm not sure this passage has ever had so much meaning for me. Someday, I'll tell you about an experience I had during my surgery. But for now, let me just tell you, all of you, that I'm sorry. I'm sorry I've been so rough on you. I'm sorry I haven't focused more on this passage and the way we should be with each other. Kimie and Ronnie, I'm especially sorry I've been hardest on the two of you. From now on, I want to show you my love rather than my hand. For I realize that Jesus may have gotten angry, but he never hit a child. And I won't either from now on. I commit to that with you. So tonight, rather than reading about another birth, I'd like each of us to share what we most appreciate about Ronnie. Then he can open his presents."

As Ronnie surveys the silent room, he sees red eyes all around. Finally, Ronnie speaks up. "Sounds great dad! And maybe another birthday joke. One that's funnier this time?" He chuckles. Lance gets up and walks over to him. Ronnie leans back, nervous his dad may strike him. Instead, with tears in his eyes, Lance kneels down and gives him a hug. Ronnie's greatest desire for his birthday was to get a brand-new baseball mitt. But that was before he had any idea that a more loving father was an option.

The Dead Entrepreneur

Paul Moser

Look, I've always been a hell of a businessman, and I can't see why my being dead should change anything. People tend to use death as an excuse for inaction, giving up, or failure. That's garbage. To me, death is an opportunity. Everything is an opportunity.

I wasn't worried about what I was leaving behind. Just moments before I cashed out, when I was lying there in the hospital bed struggling for breath, with Marianne sitting near and holding my hand while Whipper and Jackal stood by, looking at their watches and making sotto voce comments to each other about how bad I looked and how long they thought I would last, everything was crystal clear. I could see exactly where things were headed. Marianne would marry the stock analyst she met at the farmer's market last summer and, according to my private detective, had been screwing ever since. Whipper, the smarter of my two boys by a long shot, would find a way to cut poor Jackal and his mother out of the greater part of their shares of the business I built, Stradivarius Industries.

I wouldn't object even if I could—what's the point? I'm a survival-of-the-fittest person, and my family's not exempt. Whipper had already made a rep for himself in the business, not just as the boss's elder son, but because he really grasped the meaning and potential of our motto, "Who Says Exquisite Can't Be Cheap?" He'd gone beyond my original concept—a plastic violin that had a sound indistinguishable from the best, most authentic seventeenth century instruments—and sent our stock price into orbit with wildly successful extensions into the banjo, mandolin, and ukulele markets.

Twice already, he'd found ways to both lower the cost of the basic mold plastic and increase product durability, too. And without significant customer complaints.

Just about when my congestive heart failure kicked in big time, Whipper had even gotten involved with what had always been my thing—advertising. He was the one who put together a tie-in package with the Insolent Vodka people to do cable spots in 30 major markets. The final cuts were a little racy for me—party scenes with vodka flowing, thumping bass lines, and people doing pretty suggestive things with the necks of the instruments. Even while playing them.

But damn, did it move product.

Anyway, so I die and end up in hell. Not such a big surprise when you're a guy who's always refused to take shit from anybody, and who's played rough when he had to. It would be hard to defend myself as a great friend to anyone or as a family man, I guess.

It's going to sound like I'm making light of what happened, but I'm not. Let me tell you: Hell is horrible. The stench, the murky light, the screams of the damned around you, the cackling of demons, the intense heat, the chaos. Brutal stuff. That said, it's also true that I've sat through some shareholder meetings that weren't a lot better.

So, after I'd had a chance to look around a little, that's to say not just getting accustomed to my own personal tortures but zeroing in on the culture of the place, the rhythm of it, I noticed just how traditional it was. Pretty damn close to the typical picture of frenzied, wild-eyed red demons with horns and pitchforks. So, I approached my Quadrant Team Leader Demon just to ask some casual questions. I didn't want to create a big kerfuffle, but did he think that Hell had maximized its performance potential? Did he think there might be a little zazz missing from the program, slogging through Eternity like they were doing? Though I knew he had a certain flair for cruelty, the Team Leader was obviously not the smartest devil in my Chasm; yet I could tell he registered enough of my message to realize it would be worth relaying up the food chain. As it is everywhere else, covering your ass is a basic instinct in Hell.

Before you knew it, I was scheduled for a presentation to the whole Major Chasms Cadre of Beelzebub. I admit I was a little nervous, but it didn't seem like a much bigger deal than, say, one of my pitches to sell volume discount instruments to state school systems. And I had refined my message to a simple question: Are you providing your guests with an optimal, maximized pain experience?

I was a huge hit. I tapped into the dormant streak of diabolical creativity they had and got them to acknowledge there was a better mousetrap out there waiting to be built.

Of course, they wanted specifics. So, I put the question to them: what would make Hell more painful? It was a perfect setup. They gave me typical answers, like hotter fire, louder shrieking—all that stuff. After a big dramatic pause, I told them: You've got to start thinking outside *The Inferno*. For example, I said, I know some guys in California who can get you tons of frozen strawberries, and some other guys who can get you all the premium rum you want. What you do is make huge batches of strawberry daiquiris and give every resident of Hell just two ounces of the stuff.

First, I had to translate that into metric, since that's what they use in Hell. Once I'd done that, I fielded their outraged comments. Wasn't that going to make a *pleasant* experience for the Damned? Wouldn't they be happy to get a treat? Then I told them what the sharper ones had already begun to suspect. In Hell, the memory of two ounces of pleasure recently enjoyed, something that would never happen again, ever, would boost the suffering index in a big way. It was off-the-charts, brilliant cruelty.

That memory, that phantom impression of cool, sweet liquid—of crushed ice! It would drive them absolutely mad with the sense of desolation and loss and frustration. Bingo.

It wasn't long before I was senior creative consultant to The Archfiend himself and was over my head with work. Believe me, Eternity goes by pretty fast when you're organizing focus groups, running tests in the Torture Lab, and hosting evil brainstorming sessions. Interesting that once I'd hit that pinnacle—Satan's Right Hand—I began to feel dissatisfied. Wouldn't you know it? You can't keep a dynamic guy down.

I began having tempting thoughts. Had I maxed out in Hell? Had I risen as far as I was going to go? I mean, Satan had been good to me, sure, but was he going to adopt me? Turn the whole operation over to me at some point? Not likely. Retirement is not in Satan's playbook. And anyway, wasn't there room for some competition in the Hell Industry? Wouldn't Satan be spurred on to provide more and better brutally vicious services for his guests if there were another alternative destination for evildoers once they were dead? The market just wasn't going to operate optimally unless it was open to new and competitive ventures.

I knew I could get all the personnel I'd need by cannibalizing Lucifer's employee rolls. Even his HR people would follow me in a heartbeat, if they'd had heartbeats. The big hurdle, just like on earth, was getting a green light from the regulatory authority, which in this case was God, of course. He and I weren't on great terms, obviously, but I thought if I could just get up in front of the Trinity, I could maybe peel one of them off of their normally solid unanimity and stir up a discussion.

I shouldn't have worried about it. As soon as I'd made my proposal clear to the three of them and offered some examples of how I could offer superior agony, horror, and despair to my guests, I knew I had it in the bag.

Lucifer, who was waiting his turn to speak, completely blew a fuse, accusing me of treason and fraud. God the Father actually burst into peals of laughter and said, "That's rich! Especially coming from you!" The entire Trinity agreed that I was on to something big. I was sure it was because they saw that the free market would be operating and creating greater innovations and efficiencies in pain delivery, but that wasn't what was in the All-Powerful, All-Intelligent Mind at all. They praised my plan because the three of them had for a long time felt that Satan's stodgy, stale approach to brutalizing the Damned was letting many evil souls off too easy. Even more interesting, they saw my models of maximized torture as a possible *deterrent* to sinners, too. Something I hadn't even considered—but I wasn't going to complain.

So, Hell 2.0 was launched. I felt great about all of it—from my new cordial relationship with the Trinity, to the sign over the main gate, in huge letters, asking the simple question: "What's Today's Date, Suckers?"

The startup turned out to be a more powerful juggernaut than even I expected. Right away the Trinity started routing droves of depraved and wicked souls to me. It was crazy, and a little puzzling, too. Maybe they were just poking a finger in Satan's eye, for old times' sake? Whatever. I didn't really care. The main thing was, business boomed. And while Satan was trying to play catch-up using lame, tired techniques like sharpened bamboo under fingernails, I was doing real pioneering work. I began augmenting the normal-decibel shrieks and howls with old Def Leppard recordings played at head-splitting volumes, along with a continuous loop of Barry Manilow's "Copacabana". The real kicker, though, was hiring a great mimic, a woman who did a fantastic God-the-Father voice— the Creator's voice is weirdly high-pitched, incidentally—to record messages that were just audible in the din. I had her use random first names, reciting variations of a message that said maybe there'd been some kind of mistake: maybe "Domenico" should have made the cut for Purgatory, or maybe a clerical error kept "Steve" out of Heaven. Like that. From the increase in hysterical wailing in every cavern, I knew it was another genius move. The bad news was I had to let go of a couple of Supervisor Demons who got squeamish and thought maybe I'd gone too far. I sent them to the Trinity, knowing they'd get bounced right back as guests in one of our deeper caverns.

Pussies.

So now, looking back at my post-death achievements, I feel like I've got a lot to be proud of. I made myself indispensable in the cosmos, the go-to guy for afterlife punishment. But I'll let you in on a secret that isn't too much of a secret: I've already started thinking about goodness and Heaven. Fascinating concepts that need exploration. Sure, Heaven hasn't been my thing up to now, and I'd never try to claim one of those celestial mansions or anything, but still, maybe the Trinity could use some help in enhancing the appeal of Heaven to the average person. When I pitch them on it, I want to emphasize that harps and halos and all that are fine, but what will really juice up the brand? What will put butts on the seats of the heavenly auditorium?

I'm taking the "deterrence-is-not-enough" angle. Wouldn't the Trinity be happier to see souls actively *wanting* to get to Heaven, and not just avoiding Hell? What could be done to create an enhanced, sexier kind of Heaven?

I've got some answers I think they're going to like.

Flash Fiction:

Pop your Cork

The Watcher

Sue Kesler

My luck ran out the afternoon I let two men into my jewelry store minutes before closing time. They pushed the door shut, hauled out their guns and staged a robbery, and gave me a pistol whipping as a bonus. The bastards got away scot free. I was the one who ended in prison, so to speak, stuck in a body cast.

Until I got the damn thing off, I didn't have much to do besides TV. Daytime TV programming is nothing but dog pap. I soon learned most of the programs made me want to barf, too. My doc refused to let me have a beer. What with the not being able to move and only one arm free, every day seemed twenty-five hours long, which left staring out my front window my sole entertainment.

I insisted they drag my bed from the middle of my bedroom to the bay window of my second-floor space, which overlooked the street. I wanted access to a one-eighty view of the street. On most days, the highlights of my viewing would be a dog versus squirrel encounter or a two cat standoff. An occasional delivery van was a big deal and broke up the lag between morning and evening commuters. Activity on my street was zippo. The arrival of my midday meal was a big deal. My boredom meter was stuck on max. Need I say more? Our neighborhood was an example of our tedious middle-class life moving in rote routines with everyday dullness.

Early mornings began foggy and overcast, with an occasional ray of light braving the cloud cover. Today had started off the same way, but by mid-afternoon, the cars started pulling up in front of the house across the street. I'd never paid much attention to the couple who lived there. If I met the gimpy old guy on the road by the mailboxes, I'd say, "Hi." The dumpy woman, who I assumed was his wife, not so much, but I did help her with her groceries once.

I didn't see what the big attraction would be. Maybe they always had had a bunch of visitors—I'd only been the block voyeur in the past month, but I think I would have noticed a crowd like this.

Big cars and old beaters stopped by the curb in front of 2760. Soon a parade of codgers, overweight ladies, young kids with their parents, and various and sundry others were making the trip from the curb to the house. I was doing my mental evaluations of their taste in clothes and assigning values on each one on a ten scale for body type. This was the most excitement I'd had since they caged me in plaster. When their side of the street filled up, the cars hung a Louie at the corner and parked on my side. My view improved, and I kept my skills up to speed, doing instant appraisals of their jewelry and watches.

Some of the visitors making their way up the front walk were florists carrying humongous bouquets. When I spotted a wide ribbon with "Sympathy" covering the front of a large plant, I had my clue one or the other of the old folks had died. No problem in my mind—they'd already lived a long time. If I had kicked off after the beating I got, now that would be significant.

After about an hour, the comings and goings slacked off. Whatever had attracted the crowd appeared to be underway. Everyone had disappeared into the house, leaving the yard empty. My diversion sat on pause until someone decided they'd had enough and left. I shifted my weight and tried to reach into the depths of my cast to scratch. No one gave me any sympathy when I complained about how much a person itches living in a plaster cage.

A movement on the front porch ticked the corner of my eye and caught my attention. A skinny young man sat by himself, alone in the cold and damp, slumped down on a swaying old-fashioned swing. This struck me as odd behavior for someone his age, which I judged to be early twenties. His body sagged, and his hands clasped his knees, pulled back hard. His head fell back, then shot up with force. Then he lurched forward, and I noticed his shoulders shuddered. Hot damn, the guy was bawling his heart out. How come?

The scene in front of me grew weirder. Another guy appeared, the skinny one's double, only about a hundred years older with the same short, cropped hair and shoulders back attitude that reminded me of my Uncle Jake, who'd once been in the military. The old man hesitated approaching before he sat on the bench. One hand moved tentatively toward the weeping young man before he laced his arm around the other's shoulders. The kid collapsed and buried his head in the old man's shoulder. No doubt in my mind now, he was bawling, deep dark sobs. I felt my throat tighten and my eyes grew moist. The obvious sorrow of the two affected me in a way I did not expect. I had a flashback to the day a policeman rang our front doorbell and announced my dad had been killed in the freeway rush hour traffic. My world fell apart.

The senior patted the young man on the back, held him closer. They swayed from side to side. After what seemed an interminable amount of time, they parted, stood back and gazed at each other. In a single moment, both wiped their eyes on their sleeve. The elder man hugged the other again and then relinquished his hold. He turned to go back into the house. The younger watched him go and sat unmoving on the bench of the swing, head in hands. I felt sympathetic. He seemed so alone, so vulnerable.

Then he raised his head, and a faint smile widened to a grin. I think I understood why. I saw what happened. I just didn't believe it. After the older gentleman left, I thought I saw a figure seeming to appear from out of a fog, swirling and forming into a shape.

A translucent old man grew solider in front of the tear-faced occupant of the swing. The visitor plopped his ample frame down on the swing next to him and wrapped one arm around his companion's shoulder. He had a wide smile on his face and sunglasses balanced on his head. He held his pose before bending over, brushing the young man's cheek with an ephemeral kiss. As he did so, the young man became relaxed, even happy. He grinned and covered the spot the senior had touched. His face glowed. He recognized this….this whatever-it-was. I sensed he felt free to go on now. The love of the one man who couldn't have been there sustained him.

I've always been a sceptic. In my opinion, ghosts were malarkey. Now I'm not so sure.

An Atom's Tale

Rose Winters

I am a hydrogen atom. You know, one proton and all that.
How did I come to be? Well, there was this big bang, and before you
know it, poof! There I was!

I am immortal, but being the tiniest element, I've never had a
voice. I am officially a teenager today; it's my thirteenth birthday—
thirteen *billionth,* that is—so, as a gift, the Universe has granted me
storytelling privileges, just this once.

One cool thing about the vacuum of space is the lack of resistance;
I shot out and just kept rocketing. There is a lot of blackness out
there, but so much beauty. Hydrogen atoms are kind of obsessed
with each other, and as soon as I bumped into another hydrogen
atom, we were glued at the hip, so to speak. We traveled together
for millennia, twirling and dancing, sometimes streaking along the
edge of gravitational planets, bouncing off at the last minute, and
continuing on our way.

We came upon a planet with a blue haze and were instantly
grabbed up by wonderful, affectionate oxygen atoms. What a party!
All the hydrogen and oxygen atoms grabbing each other and dancing together—that was my first time as a water molecule. We became
vapor and lived in the troposphere of planet Earth for a while until so
many of us joined the party that we became a giant water drop and

fell towards earth. We quickly evaporated, and like a roller coaster, we zipped back and forth, falling, flying, falling again, until one day we turned white, and became a most glorious crystal. We flitted and floated down, down, until we landed on a soft brown hand, and a little girl with a chilled nose put us on her tongue.

What a rush! Down the esophagus, stomach... we all got split up. I was absorbed into her bloodstream and redistributed to her wet, pink lungs. Lots of my oxygen friends were there. Some of them grabbed me and we flew out of her trachea, out her mouth and into the frosty air as a soft mist. I rested for a while with my friends as a pile of white snow. When the weather warmed, a lot of my friends waved goodbye and evaporated, but I was close to the fertile earth, and a tree root absorbed me. It carried me up, up, through its sap, until I was sky high, and I became a part of a pine needle. I met many carbon atoms, as well as strings of atoms called esters that smelled fresh and sweet, like a forest.

I swayed in the breeze, basking in the warmth of a supple branch. Alas, after a few months, a big loud machine cut the tree down. The esters put out a pine scent for a long time, but my carbon friends broke apart, and the little green pine needle turned brown. The oxygen drifted away until I was alone again.

A big boot stepped on me, carrying me to a town with concrete sidewalks. I got stuck in a blob called bubble gum, and there I sat until a man with a shovel tossed me into a waste receptacle.

Lots of my aromatic ester friends were there! Not to be rude, but they smelled a bit more... pungent than my pine tree friends. To my relief, I was grabbed by some oxygen and hydrogen party buddies, and we ended up in a sweet apple core full of carbon buddies.

Eventually, a rat grabbed the apple core and ran us across the street to a warm house. A big man startled the rat, and the apple core dropped on the lawn. The carbon atoms eventually broke apart until the apple core became fertilizer for the lawn and I was evaporated along with my oxygen friends.

Along came the man, just in time to breathe us in, but I never made it to the lungs. I got absorbed into his bottom lip, and he walked in the house and gave his wife a kiss.

I know I am just an atom, but I felt that kiss, and I could tell I was a part of something important. At first, I didn't understand, but as I was transferred to the woman's lip and absorbed into her bloodstream, I was transported to a heart. But—not her heart. It was a second heart, growing in her womb.

And that is where I am now, on this, my thirteen billionth birthday. I have traveled the Universe, but I have never felt such peace and love. If the Universe will grant me one more wish today, then I wish to stay here, and be a protector, a shield, a guardian. I, a hydrogen atom, am immortal. An atom cannot die. But there is something in a child's heart that is immortal, too. Perhaps it is the soul. I do not have the answer; I am just an atom. Perhaps on my fourteen billionth birthday, the Universe will let me know.

Until

Thomas Kincaid

Your day was fine.
Until.

No, let's be more precise and more honest. Your day was feeling uncommonly livable, a splash of spring sun shone through the passing clouds and the force of your grief was not squeezing on your chest like a stiff new belt cinched two notches too tight. This was one of the better days in recent memory.

Until.

We: the heartbroken, the abandoned, the mistreated, the disenfranchised, the romantically rudderless—we know our triggers, and we obsessively calculate our daily activities to avoid them. Perhaps we take an early exit off the interstate to bypass the artisan cheese shop with the free samples and the costly memories or walk in the opposite direction of the park where he coaxed that stray, wounded tabby to a checkered blanket near his car and rushed her to the vet. The event was ephemeral, its emotional tentacles endless.

We shield our forgetless senses: evading doggedly the hum of an electric razor, the crisp effervescence of craft cider, the closing credits of that otherwise forgettable film he held your hand through on Valentine's Day, the smoky, cinnamon-strong aroma of warming fucking pancake batter.

These are the triggers. The known but avoidable heart-traps that stop you as surely and painfully as a hammer to the ribcage. That end your day.

But when you know your triggers, fetishize them, rue them, curse the cruel, pitiless god who plainly lacks the grace or power simply to let you shed them, you can extend your invisible antennae as you brave the cold world, and fairly predictably sidestep them.

Until.

To backtrack (and once a trigger has sprung, reverse is our only available gear), it was a Thursday night. How busy you were, or at least how busy you remember complaining that you were. To everyone. As if it were a hardship or a handicap. As if *busy*: that lazy, toothless, privileged, ridiculous little word was an actual affliction in the scope of human suffering. Busy? But in your "busy" days, what really did you understand about human suffering? It was a Thursday night, and you had been busy, late from work again and purposefully not addressing the consequence of domestic neglect: the mounting takeout boxes, the overflowing hamper, the cat hair collecting on the carpet near the back door (how he loved that Tabby), the unopened mail, the hastily made bed, and, a scant four blocks away, the roaming husband engaged on one end or another of some sickening act of fellatio in the fully reclined passenger seat of a Storm Blue *(gag)* Mazda Miata. You cannot bring your tongue to even say those two cartoonish words together aloud. Maaaahz-dah. Mi-ahhhh-tah. Oh, she was a sporty little slut, wasn't she?

So now, you navigate through the haze of hindsight, which proves equal parts help and hindrance. He'd been acting aloof. You'd been balancing the fateful line between distracted and derelict. Intimacy had ebbed to something occasional, jejune, tepid. Of course, the corporate merger had only been finalized for a few months, and you were desperately angling to prove your worth to the new bosses. Desperately. Desperately? How differently our tongues form the words in our cluttered lexicon once we know the acrid tang of true desperation.

Cindy Norris had texted you earlier that week about the appetizer bowl she'd left behind after the weekend dinner gathering. Yes, it was hand blown Murano glass, a fetching if fragile piece of craftsmanship, whose value in Cindy's famous sentimentality clearly outweighed its sticker price. You were going to get it back to her, for Christ's sake. It was on your expanding list of unkept promises. You'd not been home more than a couple of minutes, negotiating the extraction of your cumbersome vacuum from the cluttered hall closet, when your phone buzzed. Text message. Cindy Norris. Could she swing by? And "yes" would have been the easiest response, but it also would have been an admission of your own shortcomings, of your growing pattern of personal negligence. So, you didn't say yes, did you? No. You chose to deliver her little Italian treasure yourself. So why, to this day, do you harbor such acrimony toward simple, unknowing Cindy Norris? Why do you avoid her latest texts, send her calls to voicemail, bristle at her name, as if she were the treasonist responsible for your predicament?

You abandoned your struggle with the Dyson. You slipped on comfortable shoes. You pulled the thick blue bowl from the cupboard and cradled it with both hands. Lovelier and heavier than you had remembered. You noticed that the cat litter had been replaced. He had been home. Where was he now? No time for that. You snagged your key fob with a free finger. You made for the garage. She lived only a few minutes away, and you silently admonished yourself for making her ask a second time. You nestled the bowl neatly between your legs and buckled in for good measure. You backed out of the drive.

Your day was fine.

Until.

A client meeting downtown, and parking was always scarce. It had gone pleasingly well; it was one of your first professional triumphs since things had unraveled in that abandoned lot near Cindy Norris' house. Given the long walk to your car, you had thought to treat yourself to a croissant or muffin at that charming little patisserie on the corner, but the line was out the door, and your lately meager appetite was actually demanding something more substantial. A sandwich, you thought, and then, hell, maybe even a couple tacos? It felt good; it felt healthy to crave food. You were a little proud of yourself. You turned left at 13th, and the sun was coming out with even more force now. You were striding if not strutting, your gait had improved with the weather. Not only had you not been thinking about him, you had not even been pestering yourself not to think about him.

Until.

Had it roared past you, a blue blur doing 57 in a 45 MPH zone, it wouldn't have felt so taunting, so haunting, so daunting, so demoralizing. But there it was, ambling to a stop at a red light not ten feet from you. The same make. The same model. The same nauseatingly named Storm Blue, which you had Googled just for the satisfaction of promising yourself to one day exact a savage vengeance on that odious color.

I know your pain. I know the nightmarish dread that courses through you when sleep releases you back to unsparing consciousness, alone, in the small hours. I know how much you despise the radio, its litany of lovelorn lamentations. I know that triggers are not always obvious landmarks, but sometimes simply landmines in the fallow field of memory.

But your story doesn't end here. Not at a stoplight on 13th Street, any more than it ended where two cars were parked in tandem at that vacant lot near Sellers' Grove. You have no memory of the torrent of words you hurled at the stupefied duo, fumbling to re-dress, but pinned awkwardly against one another on that crowded passenger seat, you only know that it was pure rage, a bile extracted from your darkest place, at a hysteric volume. If memory served you just a little better, you'd probably be the only credible witness on planet Earth to what it looks and sounds like when the windshield of a Miata is utterly demolished by thick Murano glass. That's one moment, in the glare of hindsight that you actually wish you could relive.

It is going to be extremely hard. You will never avoid all the triggers. I do not sugarcoat. No simple or satisfying rescue awaits.

But one day, some difficult months from now, you will march right over one of your landmines, and it will not detonate. You will eat pancakes again. You will realize you no longer have impossible vendettas against even the most poorly named paint jobs. You will find yourself on her porch with a plate of molasses cookies and you will be overwhelmed by the sisterly support and the forgiving force in the embrace you receive from kindly, loyal Cindy Norris. You will stop telling people you are allergic to cats. You will pull up next to a little blue sports car, and rather than scrutinize the driver, you will simply turn up your music a little louder. And best of all, my misunderstood, heartsick, crestfallen darling, you will love again.

Until then.

Her Dance Card

Juanita J. Martin

Jill asked Anne about going dancing every chance she got. After all, it had been a year since Anne's husband, Tom, died of pancreatic cancer. Two single ladies, still in their prime, out for a little fun. It couldn't hurt, Jill thought. She knew this swanky club not far from where she lived. Anne had her reservations, but reluctantly agreed.

Anne whined, "Ok, but I better not regret this."

Jill grabbed Anne. "Thank you!"

Anne said, "I am too old for the club scene. What do I look like dancing to today's music with a bunch of kids? At forty-two, I'm old enough to be somebody's grandmother."

Jill, a hot looking, thirty-five-year-old, teased, "That's exactly what they'll say, too."

Saturday evening, they were on their way to the club in Jill's car, a red Trans Am. Jill turned on the radio to KJAM, "Hot Hits" 101 FM.

The music was interrupted: "This is a special alert from Brownsville Prison in Arkansas: A male patient, from the Brownsville Prison Psychiatric Ward for the criminally insane, has escaped. He is described as tall, 5'11', heavy build, sandy-brown hair, with no distinguishing marks, and clean-shaven. He is a known rapist of women and will strangle his victims. If you see or know someone fitting this description, call Brownsville police."

Anne gasped, "Oh my God!" I hope he's not in the area. He sounds extremely dangerous. Maybe we shouldn't go out tonight.

Jill exclaimed, "The police know what he looks like. Hopefully, they'll catch him before anyone gets hurt. He wouldn't dare come anywhere near the club. Lots of people there. We will be safe."

"I hope you are right. Let's get our mind off this nut and have some fun," Anne replied.

They went to Phil's Place to get their groove on. It was posh with sequined lights, disco ball, leather seats—straight out of the disco-era, except it was 1992.

As Jill and Anne arrived at Phil's, they checked their phones, got their money together, and stepped inside. They found a seat not far from the entrance and the dance floor.

Jill, dressed in a black satin dress, white party jacket and matching pumps, was sure to get a date. Anne was just along for the ride. She was dressed in a strapless, light blue dress, black shoes and black wrap.

The drinks were flowing pretty heavily, when a pair of brown eyes in a tall frame, caught Jill's attention.

Anne sat frozen in her chair nursing a Long Island Iced Tea. She was trying to be invisible, but her strapless number was catching the eyes of every red-blooded horn-dog in the place. One guy, with a tease of hair and a crude jacket to match, sauntered Anne's way. She blew him off with a negative hiss. After several dodges, Anne decided she would let one of them in her dance circle.

"Hey, pretty lady, I'm Jim. Would you like to dance?" He stretched out a confident hand.

Anne got up slowly. "I'm Anne," she mumbled. She began to feel the booze as a slow song came on. She was ready to boogie, not cuddle.

Jim started with the standard cliché. "You come here often?"

Anne felt herself warm up as the booze warmed her to Jim. "No, this is my first time. I'm here with a friend."

Jim asked, "What kind of friend?"

Anne answered, "*She* is around. Probably dancing,"

"Listen," Jim said, "I will tell you something about me and you tell me something about you. Okay, I will go first. I'm newly divorced, with no kids, and very attracted to you."

Anne said, "I'm a widow, with no kids; you're nice, but I'm not sure yet." She thought to herself, *I haven't danced with anyone except Tom before he got sick.* She missed the closeness they had, but tonight was Anne's night and despite the slow start, she was surprisingly happy.

After that first slow song, Jim and Anne owned the dance floor with their smooth moves and sexy flair. She showed those kids who was boss. After a whirlwind of fast songs, it was time to slow things down again so they could hydrate.

Jim stepped to the bar to order. In the back of her mind, Anne was concerned that she had not seen Jill for hours. That was not like her to disappear without activating the GIT or (Girl in Trouble).) If a girl was in trouble or her date was boring, the GIT was simply to hide out in the bathroom and fake illness, which usually worked.

Jim came back with drinks in hand. "Long Island Iced Tea for the pretty lady and beer for me." He noticed Anne's sad face. "You look like you are a hundred miles away. What's wrong?"

Anne answered in a scared tone, "I haven't seen Jill, my friend I came in here with. She drove us."

"Try not to be a mother hen and have a good time. I am sure she is fine," Jim answered nonchalantly. "You want me to look to see if her car is still outside? What kind of car does she drive?"

"A red Trans Am," Anne said. She called Jill's phone, but before it went to voicemail, she heard a click, as if someone picked it up. She thought she could hear someone breathing on the other end. Anne belted a cautious, "Hello, who is this?" A quick hang up followed. Anne quivered and slammed her Motorola flip-phone shut. Her next call should have been the police.

Jim came back. "No luck, darling. A car like that is quite noticeable. I circled the entire parking lot. Look, I don't mean to be forward, but it's obvious that you're stranded. May I take you home? I am sorry what I said earlier. You were concerned about your friend, and I acted like a callous jerk."

Something kept nagging Anne. Jill was not irresponsible. She wouldn't just take off, no matter how cute a guy was. *She would have called me*, Anne thought. *She would have activated the GIT if she was able to. I should call a cab and go to Jill's.*

Anne had never taken off with some stranger, either. Anne wrung her hands and started a panicky pace. "Okay, let's go." She got into Jim's silver and black mustang. "Listen, I am starving.

Can we stop at a fast-food place? I could eat that proverbial horse and his momma, too. I'm sorry, I start to twang when I get hungry. There's a place over on Lexington and 5th. It's called Donnie's. The kids love to eat there, so they open late and stay open late. The kids are always ready to eat after a night of partying. Apparently so am I."

Jim asked, "You want to listen to some music?" An announcer came on, interrupting the music: "This is a special alert from Brownsville Prison in Arkansas. A patient from the psychiatric ward for the criminally insane has escaped. His name is James Maddox. He answers to Jim."

Jim sped up. Suddenly, he was headed out of town.

The radio report continued. "He's described as a tall..."

Anne said, "Oh, I don't feel so good." She threw up in her mouth. Just then the radio went "click."

Petey

Sarita Lopez

Gerry Robison was outside, deep-cleaning the inside of his van, when the cops pulled into the driveway. His heartbeat quickened, and he wiped wet hands on a dirty rag. The van's door slid to a close just as their car door opened.

"Officers, what can I help you with?" he asked, hoping they couldn't smell the leafy green scent from the doobie he had enjoyed earlier that morning.

"We got reports of a woman screaming 'Let me go,' and 'Help!'" the first officer responded. Both cops could have passed for tweens, and the second fellow behind him didn't look old enough to grow a proper mustache, let alone shoulder a weapon.

Gerry broke into a smile, laughing with relief. "Oh, no, I promise it wasn't what you think!" He gestured toward his garage. "Do you mind if I show you what's making all that noise?"

The first officer hesitated, looking at Gerry, then back at his partner.

"I just have to punch the garage code in. It'll take less than a minute." Gerry kept his smile to show that he was just a harmless stoner and not a hardened thug.

"Keep your hands visible at all times. Move slowly. Jones, go with him," said the first officer as he narrowed his eyes.

Gerry and Jones walked to the garage door. Gerry entered in the code and tapped his foot as the door began its screechy ascent.

Officer Jones gave a nervous giggle when he saw what was caged inside.

"Fellas, I'd like you to meet Petey. I rescued him a few years ago and while he's become my buddy, he does get me into weird situations."

"Help!" screeched Petey the parrot. "Give me a cracker! Help me!"

The two cops laughed as Petey continued to squawk.

Wiping an eye, the first cop relaxed his pose. "Man, I didn't know what to expect, but it wasn't this!"

Gerry grinned. "I'll try and get Petey to sleep early tonight. Give the neighbors a rest, apparently!"

"Sorry to have bothered you. You take care now." With that, the officers waved goodbye and got in their car.

Gerry waved until the cops rounded the corner. He turned to Petey, frowning. "You, sir, give me a headache. Lucky for you, the pigs didn't catch on that parrots mimic what they hear."

And with that, Gerry closed the garage door and went back to cleaning the blood out of his van.

Nonfiction:
Decanted

Yellow Buoys, A Short Slice of Truth

Michael Wycombe

A ll parents lie to their children. I know we did. It starts with the tooth fairy, on to Santa Claus, usually finishing up with where babies come from. Eventually, the children discover the truth, but it makes you wonder why they ever believe anything else their parents tell them.

We didn't stop there. Our goal was to educate our children on how to discern fact from fiction, evidence from opinion, and, above all, think critically about what they were told by others, even their parents. We did our best to teach them to distinguish between unlikely explanations and outright falsehoods. The best stories we told them, of course, were the ones that seemed the most plausible.

Take spiders. When we first moved into the house where they grew up, we didn't have very many spiders. We did a lot of remodeling and upgrades to the house—refinished floors, remodeled rooms, and installed lots of crown molding. And suddenly, one year, we had lots of spiders. In the house, in the garden, festooning the shrubbery overnight, so the morning dew bedecked the bushes with translucent jewels glistening in the first light of day.

They wanted to know where all the spiders suddenly came from, and how come there were so many of them? Of course, I had no idea. Maybe the birds left because we had cats. Who knew? So, I explained that the spiders were breeding in the crown molding, in that little triangular gap between the wall, the ceiling, and the molding. They were somewhat disturbed by the prospect of hordes of spiders breeding behind the crown molding, but they carefully examined it and determined for themselves that there really were no viable entrances or exits that would allow spiders to breed in the space. I was pleased they took the initiative to look for evidence, but the thought still bothered them.

Next came the dinosaurs and the cavemen. Often, at dinner, we would have a competition called "Stump Daddy". If they could come up with a legitimate general knowledge question that stumped Daddy, they would get a dollar as a reward. In return, Daddy got to ask them a question. One night, I forget the question, but they did stump Daddy, so I set them a challenge: When the cavemen hunted the dinosaurs, how did they capture them? After all, the dinosaurs were much bigger than the cavemen, far stronger and faster, so how did they manage it?

Well, they pondered this for several days, coming up with all sorts of possible ways one might go about hunting dinosaurs. Maybe they trapped them in pits? Maybe they herded them over cliffs so they fell to their death? Or perhaps they used strong nets made out of vines to catch them? And possibly, because the largest of the dinosaurs were so long, they could chop off the ends of their tails and run away with the meat before the huge beasts could turn around and swat the hunters?

Over several nights at dinner, they came up with all sorts of inventive ways for puny early man to prey upon dinosaurs. Clearly, they had set their minds to solving this difficult task. As an added bonus, they also collaborated on the various solutions.

When I told them that dinosaurs died out about 65 million years before humans were around, as you might imagine, there were cries of "Foul, unfair question." But there was the lesson. You have to be able to determine if a question is even a legitimate one in the first place and even worthy of an answer. They remembered the lesson well.

And finally, we come to the one that lasted the longest. Sharks and yellow buoys. We spent a few summer weeks travelling through

Portugal, into Southern Spain, then up the Mediterranean coast into France and finishing up in Italy. We had a great time, including playing soccer on the beach in Carboneras to celebrating with the French when their team won the Soccer World Cup.

At several of the beaches where we stopped, there was a line of yellow, sometimes orange, buoys moored twenty or thirty yards off the shoreline. And the inevitable question, "Dad, what are those for?"

"To keep the sharks away, of course."

"How come they work?"

"Everyone knows sharks are scared of the color yellow, and also of orange. That's why they make life jackets orange. And all the inflatable boats are either orange or yellow. Means the sharks won't bite them while people are waiting to be rescued at sea."

"Really?"

"Of course, check it out. All the buoys you've seen are yellow or orange. So are the rubber boats. You ever heard of a shark biting an inflatable boat? You never hear of any shark attacks here in Spain where they have all these buoys deployed, but they happen all the time down in Australia where they don't put the buoys out."

This was the most long-lived story of all, lasting throughout their teenage years, certainly longer-lasting than the myth of Santa Claus. Whatever else it achieved, they always wore life jackets when they went boating, and always swam at beaches that had buoys deployed.

Now that our children are grown, they understand the buoys are deployed to stop people driving their boats and jet skis through the swimming area close to shore. But it served the purpose of keeping them safe through their teenage years when they didn't believe almost anything their parents told them—except about sharks and the yellow buoys.

As fully independent adults, they always critically assess whether any question asked is legitimate and the supporting evidence is valid.

But to this day, they still wonder if sharks really are scared of the color yellow.

No More Good Old Days

Lenore Hirsch

Those of us who reluctantly call ourselves *seniors* have much to be thankful for. Not the least of our blessings is our ability to remember how things used to be. We have seen a lot of change in all these years. Back then, if we saw a gal walking down the street deep in conversation with an invisible acquaintance, we would assume she had a mental health problem. Today it means she's having a phone conversation via wireless ear buds.

In the past, I wondered if the birthday card from my sister-in-law was mailed out of a sense of obligation or if she really liked me. Today, we have hundreds of "friends" on Facebook whom we might not acknowledge if we passed them on the street. We eagerly count the "likes" in response to our vacation photos, hoping there are more than last time. Over the breakfast table, we force our spouses to listen to the latest joke sent by a gal we met on a tour years ago. Haven't talked to her since, but we're on her email joke list.

We can easily reconnect with our high school sweetheart or the guy who bullied us in elementary school. Maybe we puff up about how pretty or smart or funny they thought we were forty years ago. This is especially satisfying if we feel neither pretty nor smart nor funny now. In the case of the bully, we might even develop a complex scheme for retribution.

The Internet has shrunk everything. Tunes that would have filled a record store can now be stored on a phone. Communication around the globe takes seconds instead of weeks. We snap and share photos in the time it took a flashbulb to pop. Without speaking to anyone, reservations can be made for dinner down the street or halfway around the world. Translation required from one language to another? *No problemo*; it's available in seconds.

There's no need to hang out in smoky bars to meet the person of our dreams. Peruse a virtual catalog of dreamy mates any time of night or day. Our only challenges are ferreting out the robots and who is telling the truth about their height, weight, and income, then finding a way to make ourselves look brilliant, gorgeous, and sexy.

With all these short-cuts for our everyday business, we ought to have a ton of extra time for leisure. We should feel a closer connection to friends and loved ones who are now so easy to reach. The problem is that all of our devices require new skills, some with a considerable learning curve. The phones, notebooks, and recording devices we are so fond of have short lifetimes. They're obsolete before we figure out how they work. We're spending more time shopping for new stuff and figuring out what to do with it. Incoming communications, whether from Aunt Betty or from one of the millions of merchants who snatch our email addresses out of cyberspace, are so frequent, we spend valuable energy sorting and prioritizing them. Little time is left actually to talk to someone in person.

Would I give up my devices and go back to the way it used to be? Never. I remember having to decide between going out with friends and waiting anxiously by the phone for an important call. Today we can do many things at once. We easily keep in touch with people all over the world. We even combine our daily walk with a chat on the phone. Just watch your step and be sure to smile at the old lady who crosses your path, looking at you with a mix of fear and concern that suggests you need a psychotherapist.

The Delay

Sarita Lopez

As a woman in her thirties who still lived with her parents, whenever they left town was thrilling. It meant I could walk around in the nude, scrounge their wine cellar, and for the next six nights pretend I was a real adult.

The night they left for Albuquerque, I made sure to leave a bowl of food out for our feral cat, Valerie, then came inside, poured myself a glass of Marciano Estate's Sauvignon Blanc and settled onto my couch. I closed all of the curtains except the one for the front glass door. I liked to keep that one open until I went to bed so my inside cat, Buddy, could peer outside at the nighttime wildlife. I never felt unsafe living away from town, although our closest neighbor was about half-a-mile away. We had a decent alarm system and RING cameras by each door. Plus, we lived in the damn Napa Valley. Eight-hundred-square-foot homes wouldn't go for over a million dollars if the area wasn't safe.

Propping my feet up, I turned on Netflix. My glass barely made it to my lips before my phone buzzed. I almost ignored it, thinking it was a text that could be answered tomorrow. This was my night of freedom and in just a few moments, my pants would be off and except for my Ugg slippers, I'd be as naked as when I first entered the world 35 years ago. When I glanced at my screen, however, I noticed it wasn't a text, but an alert from the RING, letting me know that there was movement at the front door.

That's weird. I opened the app, fully expecting to see that a bat had triggered the movement. Instead, what I saw made my blood go cold. A man was casually walking on the porch, away from my door. The video was less than ten seconds and it ended just as the man rounded the corner toward my other door.

I shrank into my couch, praying I was out of view of the front door. Yes, the same fricken door I had locked, but left the curtain wide open. My hands shook as I dialed three numbers for the first time in my life: 9-1-1.

The next few moments were a blur. I was transferred to a dispatcher named Lindsey who was patient and kind as she tried to assess the situation. I couldn't stop blabbering as I overshared that I didn't have a gun, and should I grab a knife and did she think I should make a run for the bathroom and lock myself in, and how did they get on the property when the gate was closed, and did they maybe hop the fence, but wow that's a tall fence, especially when my car was outside, and I had heard there were some burglaries in the area, and oh-my-god I was going to end up as an episode in one of those true crime podcasts, and how far away were the cops, because shouldn't they be here by now?

Lindsey asked me to turn on my RING app to see if the man was still there. I said I was scared to, as the camera light flashes on the device when the app is on. She understood and then said, if I felt comfortable, to lock myself somewhere safe. My TV was still blaring, and I didn't want to turn it off. I wanted the scary man outside to think there were several people inside. Not just one person who was thanking the big man upstairs that she had kept her clothes on, after all. I got up from the couch and casually began walking to my bathroom, pretending like I was on the phone with a friend, in case I was being watched. As soon as I was out of the front door view, I grabbed my cat, who was asleep on the floor in my bedroom, and flew into the bathroom, locking the door.

"Sarita, you're doing great," said Lindsey. "There's a bit of a delay. The nearest officer is still twenty- minutes away. We're trying to see if we can locate someone closer, but for now, just hold tight, okay?"

Twenty- minutes might have been three hours. Lindsey endured my endless chatter like a pro, before gently interrupting me.

"Sarita, I just heard that four more officers are on their way to you. All five have their sirens and lights on. You mentioned you have a gate. Can you give me the code?"

I rattled the four numbers off to her and finally, FINALLY, she let me know that the officers had opened the gate and were now searching the property. Lindsey stayed on the phone until I came out of the bathroom, where a burly cop was waiting for me outside the glass front door.

He introduced himself and I saw flashlight beams going off in all directions. He asked to see the video, and I showed him. He shook his head.

"The video's grainy, but he's definitely male. Looks to be five-foot-four. Short." He handed my phone back and said, "Ma'am, I'm going to turn off my camera now, okay?" I nodded, and he motioned for the officer coming up behind him to do the same.

"Look, you need to get a gun. And you gotta shoot to kill. This guy is gone for now, but based off this video, it looks like he's canvasing your place. Ask for Sam down at the local range. He'll teach you how to shoot if you don't know how." He stepped in closer. "You. Shoot. To. Kill."

When he seemed satisfied that the man wasn't hanging around and that he had convinced me to buy a shotgun, he handed me his card. "We'll hang around outside as long as we can and we'll keep making runs back here tonight, just in case. Call if you see him again."

When they left, I turned on all the lights outside and in. I could have stayed at a friend's house, but then what would I do for the next night? And the next? Instead, I grabbed two knives and locked my bedroom door. I shoved three clothing racks against the door and a fourth by my window. Buddy snoozed soundly all night, while I didn't sleep a wink.

The next day I stayed in bed as long as I could, not wanting to open my bedroom door. My brain felt fuzzy and my heart was still pounding since my phone first buzzed with the alert. Staying in my room wasn't helping, and I needed to get out.

I opened my bedroom door, peeked out, took a deep breath, and stepped out to the kitchen. I peeled back the curtains to see it was a beautiful, sunny day. Clenching my fists, I counted to ten before opening the glass door and stepping outside.

Nothing was amiss. No killer man waiting to pounce, no one rushing at me. Just peace and quiet, like usual. I began to clean my kitchen, tackling the dishes first. I needed a distraction, and it looked like scrubbing pots and pans was it.

After thirty minutes passed, my phone buzzed. It was a RING alert, again, for the front door. But I was right by the front door. I could see the porch and the front yard, and there was nobody there. I wiped my soapy hands on a towel and opened up the app, going to the "History" section. There, on camera, was me, from earlier that morning.

What the...?

My brain stopped being fuzzy. "Oh, shit..."

I opened up the video from the night before. The one that I had obsessively watched over and over again, trying to get a glimpse of the man's face. This time, I watched it with a fresh perspective and saw so obviously who the perp was.

It was me.

The video was me from earlier in the eve, putting food out for Valerie. If I zoomed in, I could see that the crappy video wasn't showing a man wearing a hoodie, but that it was me, wearing a huge bun with a dark headband. In fact, I had breathlessly told Lindsey, when she asked what the man was wearing, that I was almost wearing the same thing—hoodie and loose pants. But what I mistook for baggy jeans were my gray sweatpants.

The wave of relief that flooded over me was followed by sheer embarrassment. Last night, I was hiding in the bathroom . . . from me. Last night, I had five officers looking . . . for me. OMG.

I decided I could never tell the officers. They would think I was a lunatic who called the police for attention, when in reality, my RING delay was a perfect glitch of technology, mixed with a woman who watched too many horror movies.

In the afternoon, I went to town to buy a new, higher resolution security camera. After installing it, I closed *all* of the curtains and finally got to have my glass of Sauv Blanc. And that night, I slept like a baby.

Ode to Stick Shifts and Windy Roads

Stephanie Hawks

Long before learning to drive, I memorized the feel of the road in my body from the passenger's seat during the many trips to the coast from where we lived near Hawkins Bar. When I was finally old enough, navigating these curves was easy. I just had to work at learning how to let the clutch out without stalling the car.

Stick shifts, or 4-speed manual transmissions, were what I grew up with. The kind where you have to use your left foot to push in the clutch to shift gears. Mountain roads with tight corners combined with shifting through different gears are a badass combination which I love to this day and why I don't own a car with an automatic transmission.

Highway 299 in Northern California has long been known for its twists. Driving west from the top of Lord Ellis to the bottom provided the best continuous turns, one after the other. I was on a roller-coaster, swinging right and then left. The rules of driving in the mountains dictate that I brake just before entering the curve. It's a dance when I steer the car, push in the clutch, downshift to a lower gear, brake, then let off and accelerate if needed as I come out of it. Never, ever, brake in the middle so as not to mess up the rhythm and lose out on what is so fun about driving corners.

I was heartbroken when, in 1970, Highway 299 was rerouted to the opposite side of the canyon from these wonderful turns. No tight corners on that new stretch of road, no need for downshifting. No need to be ready to encounter a logging truck in the middle of a corner. I miss the old highway.

There remains a bluff with five of the most beautiful turns ever to drive near Hawkins Bar. Going west, there's a straight stretch of road, but I'm forced to slow down before entering the first curve that makes a sharp turn to the left. Driving east, I gather speed coming off the hill past Suzie Q, and it's laid out before me in a squiggly line. If I've calculated my speed correctly, I can sail through them without touching my brakes until the last one, which turns sharply to the right before the road straightens out. Those five corners are sacred to my sister and me. It is a short section, but every time we drive them, it is a reminder of just how essential a windy road with tight- ass curves is to drive when I can downshift and give it hell.

Dad's Heavy Hand

Juanita J. Martin

Another hot summer weekend was upon me as I lay asleep in my bedroom. This was a Saturday that this seven-year-old would never forget. An explosion of voices brought me to my feet. The fighting started like any other day, loud and violent. This time, I heard a crashing sound, followed by a sharp, ear-piercing scream. I ran towards the hallway. George, my half-brother, was beating on his own door from inside his bedroom and shouting at Father. "If I get hold of a hammer, I'll hit you in the head, old man. What are you doing to Mom? Let me out of this damn room!"

"Mind your business, boy, before I beat your ass." Father stood in the hallway with his hands around Mother's neck, choking her. He smelled of booze and hate. Sweat poured down his face.

Mother gasped and gagged as he squeezed harder. At that moment, I forgot I was afraid of my father. Bravery overtook me and I fought back. Grabbing his arm as hard as I could, I tried to break the death grip he had around Mother's neck.

I shouted, "Daddy, no! Let go of Mommy!" As I grabbed his arm and shook him, his eyes bulged and glazed over as if he was in a trance. I stared into his eyes, yelling, "I said no! You let go of her!" Suddenly, he trembled and released her neck. Mother slumped slowly to the floor like a withered rag doll. She coughed and gurgled, as tears streamed. George continued knocking and yelling.

I ran to the kitchen and grabbed a chair. She sat down in the hallway, wheezing and panting. After she caught her breath, I offered her some water.

Dad collected himself, grabbed his cane, and rushed out of the house. He mumbled to himself as he disappeared into the evening air. Father had nailed a board across George's door posts and jammed a nail into the lock. We got a hammer and let him out of the room.

It seemed as if George wanted revenge. "I have half a mind to shoot the son of a bitch."

George took off after Father, hoping to catch up to him. We didn't own a telephone, so we couldn't call the police. Knowing mom, she would have covered for my dad, anyway. We were alone there at the top of the hill on a dusty lane, which ended at our house.

My parents' constant fighting had grown in my small life. Neither of them would have won the parent- of- the- year- award. Our family was more like the "Monsters." I was the normal one. Mother would take her frustrations out on me. I never understood why Mother called me "bitch" and other swear words. Sometimes, I was caught between dad's heavy hand and my mother's insecurities.

It was getting late, and neither George nor Dad had returned. Mother and I cried as I held her close to me, comforting her. Mother's silence was like a weight that hung over our heads. The thought of seeing mother struggling for breath ate me up inside.

The thing that bothered me the most was the pretending afterwards. She went about her daily routine as if nothing had happened. How could she piece her life together after he tore it apart?

Did she forget? I sure didn't forget. Just the week before, Mother and I had carried my dad up a flight of stairs, with me holding his legs and her carrying his upper body, after one of his weekly drunken events. He had soiled his pants and thrown up on his shirt. After mom cleaned him up, he thanked her by wailing on her. The interesting part is his beatings never left a bruise or a mark.

Mom did things for Dad not out of love, but out of fear and a twisted sense of loyalty.

Dad did not return the entire weekend. George came home late Sunday morning and went to bed. He remained as quiet as a church mouse, saying nothing about Dad or that horrible Saturday night.

On the following Monday, as Mother walked me to school, her eyes hung low. Remains of the weekend lingered, as she fought back tears. Although I was a child at the time, I understood things I wasn't supposed to. Still upset and confused, I wanted to know why Dad was so angry.

I asked, "Mommy, why does Daddy hurt you?" She shrugged in a shy manner and looked away. "Why do you stay with him? Why don't you leave him?"

Mother's eyes widened as she gaped. She said, "How can you say these things? He's your father and my husband. Besides, I could never do such a thing."

"So! Why not? He hits you!"

"He loves me," she said half-heartedly, trying to convince herself and me, but I didn't believe it. I could not understand how someone who is supposed to love you would try to kill you. *If I had not been there, I thought, I believe he would have killed her. Maybe he might try again.*

"Mommy, I don't know anything about love or marriage, but if this is what it means to be married, I am not ever going to get married. I would never stay with a man who hit me."

Although I was a child, I spoke the truth about what I saw that Saturday. Mother was afraid of my father, even more than I was. Mother wouldn't listen. Choice was not in her vocabulary. My father's hold over her was stronger than the whiskey he drank. Perhaps the excuses she made about needing him helped soften the blows. My father's rage was like a brush fire; it smoked and burned long after whatever started it. I did not believe he loved any of us. That was a bitter pill to swallow, but one day, Mom would finally understand how Dad's behavior affected me. His anger was like a disease spreading, affecting everyone in its path.

Somehow, I had to become an example of love that Mother did not know. After all, she was a fragile bird trapped in a cage with no way out.

The moment my Dad started to hurt her, I put my childhood aside to become Mother's friend. After facing death, we changed forever. Her and I eventually grew closer because we only had each other.

For the first time, she did not see me as a child; I became her ally.

Moon Pies and Mountain Dew

Kathleen Andersen

L and survival generated more rumors than any other training we had at the Naval Aerospace Medicine Institute in Pensacola, Florida. There were rumors that you didn't get anything to eat for two days, and stories of ingenious ways that flight surgery students had smuggled food into their flight suits. Someone had heard that the armadillos in the woods had leprosy, and that at the end of the two days, a snack bar near the bus, stocked with Moon Pies and Mountain Dew soda, would be waiting for us.

We shared these stories with one another as we plotted our own food smuggling. I thought of buying a bra with large cups and filling them with M&M's, which could create a new marketing tagline: "Melts in your mouth, NOT in your bra." As the only woman in our flight surgery class, I knew this would be a novel idea. In 1980, there were not many women physicians in the Navy, and even fewer volunteered to be a flight surgeon, a doctor assigned to a naval aviation squadron. Flight surgeons underwent the same basic training with the Navy pilots, and that included sea and land survival.

The purpose of land survival was to simulate the following: you are ejected from a jet and parachute into the woods. All you have with you is your helmet, survival vest, and parachute. You must live off the land and by your wits until you are rescued. The Navy was going to explain how to do this, and then abandon us in the piney woods of the Florida Panhandle to see if we had been paying attention.

The briefing day came. We sat at small desks in our flight suits while the fit, no-nonsense Air Force sergeant gave us our instructions.

"We can't prevent you from sneaking food in for this exercise. We're not going to search you. You should be honorable and conduct yourselves like the officers you are." We looked down at our laps, chastened.

"We will teach you how to make animal traps and gillnets out of your parachute cord." He went on to show pictures of venomous snakes in Florida and how to tell poisonous berries from the non-poisonous ones.

"Unfortunately, this time of year there are no berries to eat, but there are plenty of palmettos and you can eat the roots. There are owls in the woods, and you can eat those." I couldn't imagine how to eat an owl, much less how to catch one. He finally got to the part we wanted to hear about—the armadillos.

"The armadillos in the south can have leprosy, but it is a type that is not contagious to humans, so don't worry about catching it."

Some of us exchanged glances at this. We were still skeptical. I imagined going out on a date with a handsome flyboy, and as he gazed into my eyes, I say, "There is something I have to tell you. I have leprosy from eating a sick armadillo." I decided that diseased or not, those armadillos would have free range and were safe from me.

A small zoo behind the briefing hut housed animals that past participants had captured in the woods. We walked around and peered into the cages, seeing an owl, snakes, squirrels, and other woodland creatures. The armadillo wasn't moving. Maybe it was asleep. Maybe not.

The day for land survival arrived. I was excited and a little nervous. How hungry would I get? How cold would it be? We boarded the bus in Pensacola wearing our dark green flight suits and black leather boots, with money for food after our survival exercise. The bus dropped us off in the piney woods of Eglin Air Force Base in the Florida Panhandle. I was with about ten of my flight surgery classmates. There were other groups in the woods on land survival as well, but I never saw them. The dense woods, consisting of tall pines, limited our view in every direction. The ground was covered with palmettos—fan shaped palms that grew about two feet high. The sound of a small stream caught our attention and welcomed us to our campsite, our home for the next two days.

The first order of business was to light a fire for warmth, boiling water, and cooking food, if we were lucky enough to catch anything. The sergeant came by for some parting instructions: "Someone has to be on fire watch at all times. If you catch something, turn it in to me and I'll give you some beef jerky for it." They didn't want us killing all of the forest animals during our land survival exercise.

Benny, the class slacker, immediately volunteered to be the fire watch, which meant he didn't have to go hunting for food. This surprised no one, and we all agreed. He spent all day slumped against a pine tree. If there were sloths in America, he would have been mistaken for one.

Volunteers made a gillnet across the tiny stream, and someone discovered an animal hole in the ground and designed a noose trap at its entrance. I decided to walk around and see if an animal would throw itself in front of me, sacrificing itself for a good cause—beef jerky for me. After not seeing or hearing any animals on my short hike, I concluded that they had all left the woods years ago, tired of the intrusion of these land survival classes.

On my return to camp, I was surprised to see all of the men in my group bent over and jerking something hard with their hands. I wisely decided against mentioning my observation.

They were all trying to pull palmettos out of the ground, and I soon discovered that I needed help with my own palmetto. They are *very* hard to pull up. After expending about 500 calories uprooting the thing, I ate the two inches of edible root. It tasted like a heart of palm, not bad. But with a composition of mostly water and cellulose, it provided about 15 calories, so it wasn't worth the effort. If you want to lose weight fast—try the palmetto root diet.

We had been told pine needles were a good source of Vitamin C, and if you made tea with the needles, you could prevent scurvy. Everyone else was busy tying knots in parachute cord for traps and nets, so I boiled water from the stream over our fire, added pine needles, and served it to the guys. It tasted nasty and bitter. At least no one would return the next day with bleeding gums, unless I hadn't removed all of the pine needles. . .

"Nice net, Steve!" The net maker had half finished his gillnet by sundown and stretched it across the tiny stream. Despite tying a hundred knots in the parachute line, the holes were pretty big. We could always hope that a 15-pound trout was as lost as we were and would get trapped in our net.

That night, someone in our group heard a rumor that the group of Marines next to us had captured an owl and a squirrel and had turned them in for some jerky. We were stunned and humiliated. A group of doctors, and the only thing we were good at hunting was arcane information in medical journals. I bet some of those Marines were from the Ozarks or Appalachia and grew up hunting in the forest. Their catch also disproved my theory of a deserted forest.

With no light, no food, and nothing left to do, we sat around our fire and talked optimistically about successful traps in the morning. Elliot had made a wonderful noose hanging in front of a hole in the ground. When that critter came out for its nocturnal romp, it would be caught and we would be victors. For now, it made sense to conserve our energy and just go to sleep. We made beds of pine needles and parachute silk and rested our heads on survival vest pillows. We slept as well as we could around the fire, with unhappy empty stomachs and mouths still tasting of ascorbic acid from the pine needle tea. I didn't sleep well. Too much hunger, discomfort, and snoring.

We checked our traps when we awoke. Still empty. There was probably tiny animal laughter at our crude traps during the night. But the new day brought the promise of ending our fast and returning to civilization, or at least fast food.

Our last challenge was orienteering through the woods to the bus. We paired up, and each couple had a compass. Fortunately, we had partners, or I would still be in the Florida woods. My partner, Bill, and I ended up in a swamp. Trying to walk through deep mud when hungry and sleep-deprived made it slow going, and it seemed to take longer than forever to find the bus. We were the last ones back, and probably hated by those on the bus fantasizing about burgers. But wait! Next to the bus stood the legendary snack stand! I walked over and saw mostly empty shelves. "What do you have?" I asked.

"Moon Pies and Mountain Dew," said the attendant.

"Nothing else?" I couldn't believe this rumor was true.

"Nope."

"I'll have a Moon Pie and a Mountain Dew."

For those too sophisticated to know what a moon pie is, it's marshmallow cream sandwiched between two flavorless, four-inch cardboard cookies, and covered in artificial chocolate. It tastes like you'd expect—a week old s'more.

We made our way back to Pensacola, and many of us decided to stop at Wendy's before going home. We were too hungry to care how dirty and muddy we were after two days in our flight suits and boots. We laughed at how badass we looked, thinking the Wendy's staff would react in terror when we burst in together. In truth, the cashier looked bored. In retrospect, I imagine every week a group of smelly, dirty, Navy land survivalists came by for burgers.

That completed my Navy land survival training. It was a necessary step toward the holy grail of learning to fly a Navy plane. From my survival training, I learned that if you ever eject into the pine woods of northern Florida, hope that the surviving pilot is a Marine from Arkansas, and don't eat the armadillos, no matter how hungry you are.

This Ain't Goodbye

Kymberlie Ingalls

I keep making these attempts to begin writing again. I scrawl a paragraph or two on a scrap of paper; I type a note on my phone. My lap-top sits gathering dust on a shelf at home. My attempts to be profound on social media have given way to my sarcasm and newfound trolling abilities. Bits of inspiration occasionally flitter through, but they come and go like dandelion wishes in the wind.

So, what's different about today? It's been a year—maybe longer—since I've strung together any real number of sentences, but look, here I am into a second paragraph and I haven't stopped once to check my email or distract myself by conversing with a stranger in the restaurant where I'm lunching. I'm doing it. I'm typing. I'm even writing through this ginormous platter of seafood in front of me.

This is not a drill, people.

It's been clear that I needed time away from this. From me. I needed to come to terms with what *I* want from writing versus what the world of writing has been demanding. "Write every day," they drill into us. "Write *all* the time." Write, write, WRITE! I never hear anyone say, "It's okay to not write for a while. Live your life, come back when you're ready." What is there to share if we aren't living the tales we want to tell?

Well, look at this . . . we've got a few solid blocks of words going.

Is this where I drop in the gratuitous mention of my dire health issues? What would be the purpose? Every word has to count—that's a rule. Someone had to knock some sort of new direction into me, and Death was willing to step up with a can-do attitude.

Let's map this out like a good novelist would—where was I headed, and what monumental change did my antagonist bring to my journey? These are super hard questions for this amnesiac to answer with any sort of certainty. I tend to block out the noise that disturbs me. Not in a drink-cocktails-on-the-beach sort of way, but a "I don't like this part of my life, so let's make it disappear" kind of way.

A few years ago, I was headed into isolation. I'd been withdrawing from everything and everyone around me. Apparently, the Universe had another path in mind and sent Death systematically to antagonize me—first by taking people away, then by zeroing in on me. I was sent over some sort of edge and have had to climb my way back out. I had to do this without memory, without strength to stand on.

Eventually, I ran out of words.

Last night someone lectured to us, "All writing is *good* writing!" Several of us laughed out loud. Lies; we knew better. I'd counter with, "All writing is *important* writing." Last night, I felt something that I'd been lacking for a long while: camaraderie. I completely belonged to this disruptive group of people. I felt accepted for my non-writing as much as if I'd just slammed the next Great American Novel down on the table.

The theme of my day leading to that moment seemed to be rejuvenation, and though I'd had others along this hiatus, I don't know—maybe this one stuck. Even if it's just long enough to squeak through these 800 words, I'm going to roll with it like a train song playing on the radio. I sat at the edge of the world for a little while, taking in the sounds of seabirds, the attention of hungry squirrels, and the smell that only comes from a salted ocean wave. There were smiles and bad jokes, delectable food, a fire pit just outside the window for gazing upon. A long drive to and back with songs to help me sort out the thunderous rumbles in my head.

Now we're coming to the downhill slide, so we need to find the resolution. Today, I am writing. It's still in me, but I'm not beating myself into it for a while. Maybe later, when I have an actual deadline, but right now I'm just scribbling. We won't pretend it's *good,* but we can agree that it's important.

I learned a very important thing when I was writing that last book: death doesn't always end in a graveyard. Like many things in life, we are afforded the opportunity of interpretation. I had some people in my life that no longer deserved to be there. No regrets about the time we shared, but I'm not good at severing ties, so Death and the Universe showed me what I needed to make that change. Maybe spinning me like a carousel with a drugged-up carny worker at the helm was a bit harsh, but that's the way it has to happen sometimes. I wanted it to be my time to go, but it wasn't. I had kicked everyone off my ride, but who wants to be on the merry-go-round alone?

Hey, I'm up to 910 words that I wrote in a single sitting. Maybe we should wrap this up. I think I've earned the momentary peace of mind to dig into the lunch that's waiting on the table. I feel a sense of accomplishment, which is going to disappear as soon as I sign and date this work. That's okay, though. It's a beginning, but from a familiar place.

Because life is transient, like a train song playing on the radio.

The Worst Headache

Rebecca Levy-Gantt

On June 7th, at the end of my OB-GYN residency and close to graduation, my world changed in a way I could never have imagined. At about 5:30 that morning, the phone rang. It was my mother, who was living in the apartment on the top floor of our house. Her whispery voice made me sit bolt upright in bed.

"I have the worst headache of my life over my right eye," she said weakly.

I vaguely remembered something I had been taught in medical school in a neurology lecture: "When someone says they have the worst headache of their life, that's a stroke until proven otherwise."

And now, here was my mom, using those *exact words*. I ran up the stairs, two at a time, to see her moaning, bent over the side of her bed, holding her head in her hands. I screamed for my husband to come help. Mom weighed maybe 100 pounds. He picked her up, brought her down the stairs and right into the back seat of our car. We raced in the dark to the hospital emergency room, the same hospital where I worked, and the same ER that I had been in so many times, examining rape victims, pregnant women, and bleeding patients.

This was different. Now, I was on the other side of the glass wall. Now, I was the family of someone who was sick and in need of evaluation. After they whisked my mom away, I kept trying to remember all the things I had learned about stroke, headache, and everything else this could possibly be. Since the ER staff knew me, I was able to stay nearby for most of the testing, and the radiologist came right out once he had seen my mother's head CT scan.

"She has a bleeding aneurysm and needs surgery right away, or she is going to die," he said.

"Bleeding" and "die" were probably the only two words I actually comprehended. This hospital did not have a neurosurgeon, and definitely not one that operated on aneurysms, so what did that mean? Would she just bleed until she died? Who *could* operate on her? An attending physician told me that there was a neurosurgeon who specialized in aneurysms at another nearby hospital. Time was of the essence. Two nurses placed her in an ambulance, and my husband and I followed the wailing siren to the other hospital in our car, about a 15-minute drive.

When we arrived at the other hospital, only a few minutes passed until mom was wheeled, barely conscious, into the OR. I turned to the resident who seemed in charge of everything, introducing myself as a physician.

He said, "If that was my mother, *that's* the doctor that I would want working on her."

She was in the operating room, under the knife, and in the hands of this neurosurgeon. I could do nothing. I sat down in the waiting area and cried.

Until that moment, I had been in doctor mode—getting things done, moving the patient along so that she got where she needed to go and had the treatment she needed. Now, I went into daughter mode and realized the seriousness of my mother's condition, including the possibility that she would not make it out of that OR, and if she *did* make it out, I had no idea what condition she would be in. I was in shock and felt powerless since I could do nothing to help or change the situation. I called family and friends to let them know that my mother was in surgery. I couldn't give them any information other than what I knew, that she was bleeding in the brain and it was bad. All we could do was wait. And cry.

After what seemed an interminable amount of time, the neurosurgeon came out into the waiting area. He sat down. I thought about the many times I had come out of surgery to talk with a family member of someone I had just operated on.

He said, "I'm really sorry. That was one of the worst ruptured aneurysms I've ever seen, and I've been doing this a long time."

I thought he meant that my mother hadn't made it through the surgery. More crying.

"I was able to evacuate the blood and clip the vessels. She's alive, but only time will tell if or when she may regain any of her function," he continued.

WOW. So. Many. Thoughts. Impossible to process this. Yesterday my mother was reading *The New York Times,* watching *Jeopardy*, and eating salmon for dinner. She might never do any of those things again. The tears kept flowing.

I sent my husband home to deal with the kids. It was serendipity that we had full-time babysitters and nannies. I didn't know when I'd be able to come home and resume charge of all the care and scheduling for a seven-year-old and a five-year-old. My only agenda was to sit and wait and see if my mother would survive.

I called my residency director and told him I would not be at my residency graduation day and that I would not be returning to the residency program at all. Since I had 10 days to go until graduation, I asked for a 10-day leave of absence. Since all my requirements had been met, I thought it would not keep me from actually graduating from the program. He said he would let me know.

I didn't care. I couldn't focus on anything else: not on my children, not on my husband, not on myself, not on being a doctor. I could only focus on what the next days and weeks would bring for my mother.

I was finally able to go into the recovery room, where my mom was attached to a ventilator that was breathing for her. She had no fewer than six other tubes and drains attached. Her head was bandaged. She was comatose, completely unresponsive, and looked small and fragile.

I remembered my days as a third-year medical student as that old feeling of being so afraid of the ICU returned. This was ten times worse. I sat in the black cushioned chair next to her bed, trying to figure out what all the beeping monitors were doing. Knowing some, but not all, of their functions made everything more difficult.

I had always had a somewhat strained relationship with my mother, and having nothing to do but sit and think about her stroke and our relationship made the situation untenable. But I was determined that, if and when she woke up, I wanted her to see me so she would not be scared. So, sit there I did.

I sat in the black chair for what felt like weeks but was actually days—eight days, to be precise. I sat there listening to monitors and getting to know the nurses, residents, and attending physicians. On day eight, my mom, still with tubes and lines coming out of every orifice (including her skull) opened her eyes. As if waking up from a long nap, she looked right at me, without fear, without pain, and definitely without recognition. Mom looked at me with annoyance, as if this hospital, these people, and definitely these *tubes* were inconveniencing her. I had seen this look many times before. And to see that very recognizable look of annoyance after an aneurysm surgery, and after days in a coma, my first thought was that maybe she was still inside there somewhere. The thought was reassuring, but before I had a chance to speak, she fell asleep again. For another three days, I sat.

While at her bedside, I thought about all the clichés: life is short; find your happiness; happiness is a direction, not a place. I thought about my life up to that point—my family, my kids, my situation. Up until that moment, I had not been introspective. I wasn't even very emotional, except where my children were concerned. Watching my mother fight for her life in a hospital bed created emotions and reflections I did not know were in me. I promised myself then to always work to find my happiness and hoped I'd have the chance to help my mom do the same.

Those three days, I sat with my thoughts and memories. I remembered the time I was 12 and about to go to my first girl-boy party. I thought I looked cute in my new blue and white polka-dot dress and emerged from my bedroom ready to go.

"You're not wearing *that,* are you?" my mother had asked, completely crushing my 12-year-old spirit.

I contemplated the time when I was 18 and beginning to apply for college. My grades were great, I wanted to travel, and I started looking at college catalogues. When I was filling out the applications, my mother looked over my shoulder and snatched me back to reality.

"We'll get you a used car, since you'll be living at home and commuting to college. Unless you plan to study pre-med, pre-law, or engineering, we aren't going to pay for an out-of-state university."

I thought about the many times she bluntly told me exactly what she thought, with no regard for hurting my feelings. And I considered how often people had told me that I looked, acted, or sounded like her. I wondered if these were the qualities I shared.

I also thought about how willing she had been to help when I decided to go to medical school and how she showed her love for my children. I realized that although I did not appreciate her stringent tone or unfiltered words, her heart was in the right place. I always knew she loved me. Maybe when she woke up from all this, *if* she woke up from all this, there would be some kind of change. Maybe I could help it along. Maybe I needed to be the change that I wanted to see in her.

At the end of those three endless days, mom woke up for good. She was in the ICU for three weeks, in the hospital for four more weeks, in rehab for 18 months, and in assisted living for a year before she could return to living somewhat independently. She lived an additional 22 productive years, and I was never more than a mile away from her. She saw my kids grow up and met her first great-grandchild. She traveled, spent time with friends and family, and had a huge birthday celebration when she turned 90. She was still often annoyed at the feeling that she was infirm or dependent on me. But something was different about her attitude. I was different.

Holding to the vow I made while I sat in the black chair by her hospital bed, I had learned to appreciate her presence, her experience, and her advice. Her bluntness did not impact me as it had in the past. I actively sought and found my happiness, and I believe that I helped her find a bit of hers.

My Beloved Ice Pick

Paul Moser

I ignored their remarks at first. After all, my fellow college freshmen were bound to be self-conscious and a little defensive. Everything was strange and intimidating in those autumn days, as we moved into our dorm rooms, adjusting to a new life: unpacking, organizing, registering for classes, getting to know each other. But after a month, my situation was clear: I was a cultural pariah. How did it happen? How did a social stink bomb come to fall directly on my head? I wasn't nerdier, or more awkward, or uglier than anyone else on that dorm's second floor. But my problem went deeper than any of that. It was about my stereo.

It wasn't as if my stereo was hurting anybody; it was just an innocent, mediocre machine, one that was common in 1967. It was a suitcase-like contraption made by Magnavox, featuring a fold-down turntable and hinged, detachable speakers at each end. It was reliable and boring. I thought the sound quality was pretty good. I had a headset that I used when my roommate was around, so there was no problem there. I was happy enough to play the few albums I had brought with me from home: Sergeant Pepper, The Doors, Simon and Garfunkel, Buffalo Springfield.

I was happy enough, that is, until one night after dinner when I was about to head to the library to study. The corridor was suddenly filled with piercingly loud, exquisitely crisp rock music. I knew immediately it was the new album from the Doors, called *Strange Days*. It sounded *fantastic*. Once out in the corridor, I could tell the sound was coming from a room just a few doors down, the room of Peter Barka and Rob Hammersmith, two guys from Connecticut with whom I had exchanged little more than casual greetings.

I stuck my head in the open door. Peter sat at his desk, smirking at me. "Too loud?" he said, with a look of detached amusement. Peter was a thoroughly ironic soul, it seemed to me, his smile mischievous, his eyes even more so as they darted around under his carefully coiffed mop of brown hair. He was lanky and angular, looking almost comical in a desk chair too small for his frame.

"No, No, it's great! The new Doors album, right?" I shouted in response.

"Right."

Once we got that straightened out, there was no doubt about the next topic of conversation. Arranged on the bookshelves above his desk was one of the most impressive collections of stereo components I had ever seen. Peter saw me gawking at all the fancy lights and meters and God-knows-what, and he turned down the volume so he could fill me in. His voice had a zealous, almost missionary tone, tinged with the kind of resignation necessary in casting pearls before a swine like me.

First there was the Fisher 440-T receiver—gotta have that kind of power to drive the KLH Linear Dynamics speakers. And naturally you want the Pioneer PLX-1000 turntable with its $50 diamond stylus to bring pinpoint sound to the system. Not to mention the equally pristine sound offered by the TEAC A-2300-SX reel-to-reel tape recorder. "I'm pretty pleased with it," said Peter, oozing high-fidelity self-satisfaction.

"Amazing," I said. "You've really got a great thing here."

There was a longish pause. "So," he said. "What do you do for music?"

There I was, a deer caught in the headlights of the Personal Humiliation Bus. I had to make light of it, if such a thing were possible

with someone like Peter. "Oh," I laughed. "I've got a little portable unit. It does the job for me—even though I think the whole thing is worth about what you paid for your turntable stylus. Ha-ha."

"Oh, okay," he said, straining not to sound condescending. "I'll crank up the sound on this system anytime you like." He flashed a rakish grin.

"It's a deal. See you later!" I said, fleeing back to my room. I dawdled there for a few minutes, just to listen to more of that astounding sound quality before heading to the library.

That was just the beginning, of course. A few days later, Peter and his roommate Rob knocked on my door, ostensibly paying me a friendly visit, though they obviously wanted to check out my sorry little stereo. "So, this is the thing itself," said Rob. "Made by Magna-sucks."

"Now, be nice," Peter said, his voice dripping with treacle.

I gave a forced laugh. "Hey, stereos have feelings, too," I said.

Peter noticed that in my small collection I had a copy of the new album, *Buffalo Springfield Again*.

"You can borrow it if you like," I said. "I'll bet it'll sound great on your system."

"Oh, no thanks. Really." He exchanged a glance with Rob. "We better get some studying done if we don't want to flunk our first mid-terms. See ya."

Pretty soon my room became a stop for every budding audiophile on our floor, like I was part of some Grand Tour of Oddities. Guys I didn't know very well would come in, take a look at the stereo and say something like, "So this is the monster, huh?" Or "Does it actually work?"

It wasn't like life on the corridor was all about sound systems, of course—there were plenty of memorable people and events. There were the usual guys who made a ritual of throwing up on the hallway carpet every Saturday night, and the few guys who managed to get girls into their rooms. There was the serious ongoing poker game frequented by affluent kids who could afford to lose a hundred dollars a night and not be forced to drop out of school. There was the guy who insisted on standing in the middle of the corridor every Thursday night, praying for everyone's soul for about a half-hour. And there was Rob, Peter's roommate, famous for sleepwalking. "Luckily, he's usually too confused to get out of the room," Peter said, laughing. "But I had to chase him down the corridor at about 4 a.m. last Wednesday. I was afraid to wake him up, you know, with all the stuff I've heard about the dangers of waking a sleepwalker too abruptly and all."

As part of this strange circus in our corridor, my stereo and I had established a solid reputation for backward eccentricity. I thought I'd finally gotten used to it until the day I was standing in Peter's doorway listening to Jefferson Airplane's *Surrealistic Pillow* and asked him if he would be willing to lend me the album sometime.

He was incredulous. "You're joking. Seriously? You think I'd let you play one of my albums on your ice pick?!"

I thought he might be kidding, but his tone said he wasn't. "You're figuring that my playing your record on my stereo a couple of times will ruin the record? Is that it?"

Peter looked at me with pity. "Of course, it will. No offense. You understand the problem."

"Well, no, I don't, actually. But hey, it's your record. Couldn't hurt to ask."

But it did hurt to ask. I steered clear of Peter and Rob for a while after that, feeling like my grudge would dissipate after a week or so.

As it turned out, I didn't have that much time.

One night soon after that exchange with Peter, I was lying in bed, trying to get to sleep while enduring the snoring of my roommate. I was just drifting off when the door opened and Rob appeared. I was speechless, not just because I was sleepy, but because Rob was wearing nothing but a pair of Jockey briefs. He didn't look at me, but turned to his right, standing directly in front of my stereo.

It took a moment for me to grasp the situation: he was sleepwalking, of course.

"Rob?" I said in a low voice. "Shouldn't you get back to bed?"

He didn't answer me, didn't even turn to face me. Because I could see only his back, and couldn't see his hands, I didn't realize what he was doing until I heard the gushing, splattering sound of liquid falling. He was relieving himself on the turntable. I froze in shock. This wasn't happening.

In what seemed like just a few seconds, he had emptied his bladder, and, as if to add insult to injury, he reached to his right and flicked the switch that ordinarily would raise the tone arm from a record and return it automatically to its cradle. I could hear the stereo clicking away, the tone arm wandering over the empty, sopping-wet turntable before returning to its position.

"Rob!" I said, much louder now. "What the hell do you think you're doing?"

He turned back toward the door, and looking sideways at me with a little smile, raised his hand and waved. Then he was gone.

I lurched after him and grabbed him by the shoulder. "Rob! Do you know what you just did? Are you nuts?"

He was glassy-eyed, blinking slowly. "Have to get to bed," he said dully. "Gotta sleep."

I was furious, but what to do? Wake Peter up, wake up the whole corridor? I didn't do any of that, probably because somewhere inside, I at last had adopted the same opinion of my stereo as the others. It was junky. So, who was going to care?

I retreated to my room, confused and enraged. The question was, had he actually been sleepwalking, or was he carrying out an elaborate prank, one probably endorsed by just about everyone in the corridor? I stewed over that question as I found a towel and began mopping up the mess. Nearly all the instrumentation, as well as the underside of the turntable and its machinery, was soaked. There was a puddle on the floor. Once I'd sopped that up, I pulled another towel from a drawer, got a big glass of water from the bathroom, and washed the whole machine as best I could. It seemed like a lost cause—maybe because it was. I was upset enough that I didn't sleep much. My rage dueled with my poor self-esteem, now personified by the "Ice Pick." How could I be upset about someone vandalizing a piece of junk? But on the other hand, how could I *not* be upset?

Early the next morning, I showed up at Peter and Rob's door, sullen and sleep-deprived. As I expected, Rob expressed disbelief that he might have done such a thing. His deadpan expression held, but barely. "I'd never do a thing like that. Come on," he said, with what seemed a lot like mock sincerity. Both he and Peter looked like they were stifling laughter.

I seriously considered threatening to dump a chocolate milkshake on Peter's Pioneer PLX-1000 turntable, but thought better of it. Why escalate this thing into a war that no one would win? It would be mutually assured destruction.

Instead, I took my Ice Pick to an electronics repair place. The guy behind the counter took a quick look. "What happened here?" he said.

I sighed. "It's a long story."

He shook his head. "Better you don't tell me," he said. "But you know what? It'd be cheaper for you just to buy a new one for the money it'll cost to clean the sludge out of this one."

I told him I didn't care. I wanted to go ahead and get it cleaned up. Sentimental reasons, I told him.

I picked it up six days later and set it up in its usual spot in my room. No one in the corridor ever mentioned it again. At the end of my junior year, I gave it to my younger brother. It ran beautifully for years.

Musalacon Summers

Lance Burris

M usalacon was a hundred-acre ranch located outside the Northern California town of Cloverdale, where, in the early nineteen
fifties, I spent two of the most formative years of my childhood.
The ranch has since been scrapped to make way for a soulless,
mid-century subdivision.

Musalacon's creek flowed freely in winter and early spring, when
poisonous-looking yellow and orange fungi sprang up along its banks.
I delighted in floating small, hand-carved boats on its cold, clear water.
The riverbed was dry the remainder of the year and separated a large
meadow from the adjoining fruit orchards, in which I picked prunes
to earn enough money to buy toy soldiers at the local variety store.
On hands and knees, I worked alongside American migratory workers
who followed the harvests and were later replaced by immigrant
pickers under California's Bracero Program.

When my family first moved to Musalacon, the remodeling of what
was to be our side of the main ranch house was not yet complete. My
parents and I lived temporarily in what was called the "Woodchoppers
Cabin", where, at age ten, my imagination and related powers of
visualization began to blossom. One morning my parents went into
town to have breakfast, since our future kitchen was still unserviceable.
I remained behind in bed propped up on pillows watching a daddy
long-legs scramble along its web in the bedroom's high ceiling while

listening to *The Breakfast Club, Smilin' Ed McConnell,* and *Big John and Sparky* on the radio. During this dream time, I dunked sugar cookies in a willow-patterned cup filled with tea and milk, which had been prepared by my mother. Later, upon moving into my bedroom in the main house, I also listened to the broadcast of *Bob and Ray, Sky King, The Lone Ranger,* and science fiction programs such as *Tom Corbett—Space Cadet* and *Dimension X.*

My bedroom in the main house was largely furnished by the owner. It contained old prints and maps, an antique organ which I could not play, and several musty sets of nineteenth century encyclopedias from which I learned a lot of out-of-date information (such as Mt. Atlas is the tallest mountain in the world) and read voluptuous poetry by the Rosettis. I read one of the more florid Rosetti poems out loud in class, being completely oblivious to its "fruits and flowers" sexual allusions.

Being an only child who lived on a ranch outside of town, I had no one to play with during the long, hot summers. Hours were spent in my bedroom stretched out on the rug looking up at the battlements of my Masonite castle, the parapet of which was manned by my prized collection of Crusader knights clad in silver helmets, chain mail hauberks, and white surcoats emblazoned with red crosses. As I lay on the floor, their painted pink faces peered down at me through the crenellations. I would stage noisy sieges, some of which could be heard through the party wall by the landlady, who was initially concerned something terrible was happening to me.

Many of my lead soldiers were given to me as gifts. However, the most exciting acquisitions occurred during the Christmas season when my parents took me to San Francisco, where we would make the rounds of the Union Square department stores, pausing to inspect each of the magical window displays. Along the way, we would stop by Podesta Baldocchi to inhale the intoxicating pine scent of the Christmas trees and decorative wreaths. The high point was our visit to the City of Paris, known for the enormous Christmas tree that filled the store's multi-story rotunda. We would take the elevator up to the toy department, where I gazed in wonder at the store's collection of lead soldiers displayed in glass cases beyond the reach of children's eager hands. Some were freestanding, while others stood rank upon rank in formation. Still others were neatly aligned in glossy burgundy or green boxes. There were blue and grey uniformed soldiers from the American Civil War, French Legionnaires, Arabs with scimitars, bagpipe-playing Highlanders, Beefeaters with halberds, and, of course, my favorite knights in armor.

The owners of the ranch sponsored a young Frenchman who was a member of the Lanson champagne family in Rheims. When I first met François Lanson, he was only nineteen. I was struck by his foreign appearance. In the middle of the summer, he wore a dark suit, white dress shirt with French cuffs, and a hounds tooth deerstalker's cap, of the kind worn by Sherlock Holmes and called a "fore and aft" by the British. His manner of dress was surprising because of its formality and inappropriateness in the summer heat. His parents had sent him to California to study wine marketing at a time when many of the vineyards remained derelict as the legacy of Prohibition. In a memorable exchange, which occurred while he watched me play on the floor, François asserted my Crusader knights were French. I immediately corrected him, saying: "No, they are English!" At the time, I had no idea that Richard the Lion Heart of Robin Hood fame was a Norman who spoke French, and that the Knights Templar were, for the most part, French, as indicated by the name of their leader, Jacques de Molay.

One of my outdoor activities consisted of making the rounds of the ranch dressed as Robin Hood in a costume made for me by my mother. The costume consisted of a green leather cap fitted with a long, pheasant tail feather. I carried the English long bow made by my father, slung a green burlap quiver full of target arrows over my shoulder, and slid the leather sheath of my prized hunting knife onto my belt. Occasionally, I would further arm myself with my handmade wooden sword and painted cardboard buckler.

My walkabouts would begin with a visit to the meadow where I shot arrows at the bales of hay or at the red-tailed hawks which lazily circled above, my arrows falling short and plummeting back to earth. I would then follow the narrow deer trail up the heavily forested hillside in search of that sunlit glen where a band of Merry Men, clad in Lincoln green, could be found feasting on roast venison washed down with nut brown ale. Of course, I never found that secluded spot, which allowed the search to continue.

On occasion, I would don my mail-order Daniel Boone coonskin cap, stick my handmade flintlock pistol in my belt, to which was attached my beloved hunting knife. With Wham-O slingshot in hand, I would set out to find that elusive band of Mohicans. While they too were nowhere to be found, their existence was clearly established by the many arrowheads found on the ranch.

On other occasions, I would take daytrips to the Russian River while my father was at work. My mother would drive us to a friend's house, which was within walking distance of the river. Her friend, Jo, would accompany us as we trudged north in the heat of the day to the point where the Redwood Highway bridged the river. I wore loosely woven leather sandals on those outings. I can still feel the cool sand between my toes as I descended the steep embankment which was cast in deep shadow by the iron bridge. During the descent, I could not escape noticing the obscene and anatomically explicit graffiti which some teenager had scrawled in charcoal on the concrete abutment. A rocky beach lay at the bottom of the incline. There, a group of older women conversed in Italian, while picnicking beneath a protective umbrella. As a young boy, I was shocked by the whiteness of their Rubenesque bodies, overflowing their shiny, black bathing suits.

As the river flowed southward, it rounded a sharp bend, creating a whirlpool which broke into small eddies as the water welled up from the bottom, slowed, and then ran deep and green in the shadow of the bridge. From time to time, the void beneath the bridge was filled with the thundering echo of a passing eighteen-wheeler, whose driver greeted the swimmers below with a blast of the truck's air horn. The iron bridge spanned a rocky gorge where white-skinned boys in cut-off jeans could be seen scrambling up the cliff face. At the top, each waited his turn at the metal pipe attached to a rusty cable affixed to the underside of the bridge. The first in line would grasp the pipe and, with a whoop, leap from the rocky precipice, arc over the river, and, letting go, momentarily freewheel through the air, before noisily splashing down and disappearing beneath the surface of the water. While I had swung on the cable several times, I preferred to swim across the current, transit the whirlpool, or dreamily drift downstream as the river rapidly accelerated, turning golden as it raced over the rocky shallows and swept beneath the branches of the willow trees lining the river.

After the day's outing, my mother and I would return to Jo's house. Feeling fresh and clean, we would drink sweetened iced tea and eat homemade brownies as a perfect ending to a perfect summer's day.

The ranch's meadow and orchards are long gone. So is the Russian River's old iron bridge after being bypassed by the Interstate Highway System. Yet, my memory of those Musalacon summers remains vivid, because the events took place in an analog age, when a young boy experienced the world directly, and his imagination filled his days with adventure.

My Calistoga

Joanne Jagoda

I 've been going to Calistoga every year since I was four years old, and I just turned seventy. When I grew up, we were the kind of family who never made it very far on vacation from our home in San Francisco's Richmond district. My father, though a sweet and wonderful man, couldn't read a map if his life depended on it and getting lost was expected. He could have really used a GPS or Google maps! In the 1950s, money was tight for my parents, German immigrants who had fled Hitler. Unlike my children, who by the time they were twenty, had already travelled extensivelyto exotic worldwide locations, backpacks in tow, our world wassmall.

As long as a swimming pool figured in the vacation, we were happy kids.

San Francisco in the summer, as Mark Twain famously pointed out, can be a cold place. On many days, thick fog wafted in and lingered with a biting breeze, where we lived a mile from Ocean Beach. My mother's mission was to get her pale-faced brood out of the city to warm sunshine where we could brown like plump chickens. My parents had heard about Calistoga in the Napa Valley from other immigrant friends. Since the late 1800s, spas had existed in Calistoga, promoting the natural mineral water's restorative powers. In the 1950s, Calistoga became a mecca for San Francisco's Jewish immigrant families because of the good weather, mineral pools and the scenic location. We ended up going to a no-frills resort, Little Village, every summer throughout my childhood.

Calistoga was a two-hour drive from San Francisco, if my father didn't get lost. He would bring us on Sunday, go back to the city to work, and return on Friday night for the weekend. I can still see him in his undershirt in the garage, sweating and swearing on the Sunday morning we were leaving, cramming every inch of the two-tone green Plymouth Savoy with everything we needed for our two-week vacation. We kept bringing him things we thought we couldn't be without, and he managed to fit it all in the packed trunk. We drove off in a shroud of fog, but by the time we reached the Golden Gate Bridge, the sun was poking through the thick gray layer of clouds. The three of us kids skirmished over who got to hand the man the quarter to cross the bridge. I insisted it was my turn. (It was always my turn.)

We were three in those years before my younger brother was born. My older brother sat shotgun in the front seat, dominating the radio, tuning in to KYA. My sister and I sat on either side of my mother in the backseat. She held a bag or two because one or both of us would get carsick, and had 7- Up in a glass bottle to soothe our upset tummies. The roads were bumpy, not helped by my father's driving, and we could smell cows lounging on the side of the road.

When we finally arrived at Little Village, my sister and I dashed off to the swings. We loved those swings where we could stretch out our sturdy little legs and touch the tallest branches with our tiptoes. We felt like we were flying. My father's first job before unloading the car was to negotiate the cost for the two weeks with the resort owner. In those days, we could stay in a simple cabin without air conditioning that *did* come equipped with a flyswatter, for the princely sum of maybe $60 a week.

The first thing my mother did was attack the bathroom with Lysol. The cabin had a bathtub with permanent rust stains, probably from the minerals, and when you ran the hot water faucet, you could detect the rotten egg smell of sulphur. My parents loved taking scalding mineral baths and didn't care that the tub wasn't fancy.

My dad unloaded the car, and we grudgingly carried in the battered suitcases and overflowing boxes. Then we settled in the shade on the cabin porch for the picnic lunch my mother brought: deviled egg and tuna fish sandwiches from the red plaid cooler, along with containers of pickles, carrots and olives and cold drinks from a thermos.

After lunch, we couldn't wait to trek to Pachateau's, the huge public pool, taking a shortcut through the back field behind the resort. We sweltered in the afternoon heat, holding our inner tubes, while the weeds and burrs stuck us through our rubber sandals. We paid 25 cents to use the pool during the week and maybe 75 cents on weekends. My mother would slather us with a coating of Sea & Ski, and then we spent hours splashing in the pool. We loved those hours at the pool.

Heated by a natural geyser, the pool was warm like a bath. It was divided by a big black rubber rope separating the shallow and deep ends. Pachateau's attracted a lively international hubbub of families, many of whom, came for the day from San Francisco, to picnic on the lawns and swim. On Wednesdays, when the water was too hot because the pool had been cleaned and re-filled with geyser water, we would go to Alder's, which we did not like as well. Alder's was the site of the Calistoga Spa today. Eventually, Little Village put in their own pool, which we preferred because it was cold and perfect for the many hot days.

Because we went to Little Village every year, we would meet up with the same families. We came from different backgrounds, some of us Jewish, others boisterous Italian-Catholic families, but we all got along well. The kids played endless shuffleboard and ping-pong games. We devised elaborate hide and seek adventures and the boys got into trouble with slingshots.

We entertained ourselves with paper dolls and comic books we bought in town. A couple of summers, I organized a talent show, and the parents sat in the "audience" while the kids did little singing and dancing acts. The resort owner treated us to ice cream after the show. That was a big deal.

The main form of evening entertainment was strolling to Main Street in our sundresses and buying a gooey marble fudge ice cream cone at the Village Green for five cents. If we came during the Fourth of July festivities, we would go to the morning parade featuring home-grown floats and prancing horses with elaborate silver decorations. At night, when it cooled down, we'd head to the county fair. There were carnival rides, candied apples, cotton candy and 4-H exhibits. I threw a nickel on a plate and won a duckling, which we took in a box back to San Francisco. We then deposited it in Spreckels Lake in Golden Gate Park. My sister and I have a long-standing argument over who won the duck. I know it was me.

Some summers, if something good was playing, we went to the Ritz, the tiny movie theater. I'll never forget the magical night when we saw *West Side Story*. All the kids were in love with Natalie Wood or Richard Beymer, and we pretended to be the Sharks and Jets dancing in the streets after the movie.

What is it about this little town that, after so many years, continues to pull us back like a primal force? Just spending a few days relaxing and enjoying the natural beauty of the mountains and vineyards, even the smell of the air, helped us weather tough times, like my breast cancer diagnosis and my husband recovering from heart surgery.

Main St. has felt the strain of the recent fires which hit the Napa Valley hard and has suffered during the pandemic. It is just coming back to life now after tough months and hopefully new businesses will open. We have recently been to our favorite place, the Calistoga Spa, and despite restrictions because of the pandemic, it was lovely being in the uncrowded pool. Even though we wore our masks, we enjoyed taking our early morning walks in the vineyards, strolling in town and visiting favorite restaurants. Though many things have changed, and I can no longer get a gooey five cent ice cream cone, rich memories of my childhood summers in Calistoga still fill me with joy, and I never tire of coming back and making new memories.

Darlene

Kathleen Andersen

Darlene sat in the examination room and listened to the full hier-archy of physicians and surgeons discussing her condition. She sat quietly, her head gently shaking from side to side, while the complex discussion circled around her in a vocabulary that, to her, was incomprehensible.

For years Darlene had lived with dystonia, a mysterious condition that caused her neck muscles to spasm, jerking her head back and forth. Watching her, it appeared to be almost constant. Despite this disability, she worked as a grocery store clerk. As one of the medical team, I wanted to help her.

Darlene's primary doctor had initially referred her to a neurologist. She had had a thorough workup, brain and neck scans, and was ultimately referred to the Department of Neurosurgery at the University Hospital, where she had been examined by a medical student, an intern, several surgical residents, the chief neurosurgical resident, and now was being seen by the neurosurgical attending, who occupied the apex of this surgical pyramid.

Dr. Brunswick had examined her and reviewed her imaging scans with the radiologist. The diagnosis was made and a treatment plan developed.

He sat across from her and leaned forward.

"Darlene," he said. "From the tests you have had, we can tell which nerve in your neck is causing these twitches and spasms. I can perform surgery on your neck and cut this nerve. It will stop these unwanted head movements. The surgery is not dangerous or painful and your hospital stay will be short."

We all watched Darlene's face for her reaction to this wonderful and encouraging news. Her face did not change. Her affect was flat, and she said nothing, her long graying brown hair moving gently around her face.

"Do you have any questions about the procedure or what to expect?"

"No," said Darlene. More silence. Her head shook uncontrollably.

The intern offered, "Medi-Cal will cover all of the expenses, so the surgery will be free for you. If you come out to the desk, I will help you schedule the date."

"I don't want the operation," said Darlene. This statement was followed by multiple explanations and reassurances. Darlene was quiet, then finally said, "If there is no head shaking, there is no Darlene." A stunned silence. A few of the doctors reiterated what was said, but her decision was firm.

Slowly, the doctors left the room, the most senior followed by the most junior, and all were shaking their heads, along with Darlene.

My Yellow Dress

Julie Ann Schrader

My yellow dress. Dark yellow. Honey-colored, really. *Not* a hand-me-down from my big sister. I'd spent hours over my Grandma Lala's treadle sewing machine, rocking that iron foot pedal forward and back. Stitched with my own hands, that dress was part of me. If my yellow dress could speak, it would announce to everyone that it belonged to me, and that no one could take it from me. My Grandma fashioned a tiny hip-pocket with lace trim.

I frowned. "The pocket's way too small, Grandma."

"It's not really meant to hold anything, my darling. It makes your dress stand out from all the rest." She smiled at me in that way of hers that sent waves of love washing over me. The finished product covered me from neck to wrists, while the hemline crept halfway up my thighs.

At breakfast I couldn't swallow my soft-boiled egg. I tried to cover the knot in my throat with a silky scarf, but that ended up on the floor in a pile of discarded shoes. Nothing looked right. I decided to wear nylons even in the oppressive Midwestern heat. They would lend me an air of seriousness about higher education, which I needed for this day, especially on this day—the day my yellow dress and I were meeting with the University of Wisconsin deans.

Dad's silence thickened the air in the car on the I-94 to Madison, Wisconsin, leaving us each with our own thoughts. I imagined that if he did speak, he would accuse me of being an ungrateful eighteen-year-old, throwing away the gift of higher education that my parents had worked so hard to provide—that my Dad had been deprived of during the Great Depression. He worked a toothpick between his teeth, noodling it around with his tongue from side to side.

Occasionally, he grasped it between thumb and forefinger to prod some hidden morsel. I had learned to read his level of frustration by the volume of his teeth-sucking. This day it was turned up a few decibels.

My university grades had plummeted into an abyss in my first year. I stared out at green and yellow fields sliding by for two hours, eating the flesh around my fingernails and praying for redemption. Until that morning, the letter with the official University of Wisconsin stamp hadn't seemed real. They were kicking me out.

With open car windows begging a breeze, I could measure the mugginess from Lake Michigan by how much frizz claimed my hair. That morning I'd laid the whole length of it on the ironing board, holding handfuls down while wielding the hot iron, pressing them into obedience. The sodden breeze only served to push the liquid air around us with little relief. By the time we reached campus, those stick-straight strands had expanded into a tent of anxious tendrils.

Bascom Hall housed the deans' offices, situated on an impressive knoll surrounded by too-perfect lawns and bushes. White pillars overlooked the arched entryway. We pulled in.

My often-silent Dad, with his tender heart, turned to face me. My heart jumped. He removed his toothpick.

"Well, Jelly Bean, what do you have to say for yourself?" In that moment, I needed to come up with something worthy of forgiveness, and quickly. He'd used my childhood nickname, which was encouraging. Even so, as I searched for words, my mouth came up empty. I shrugged.

His brown eyes searched my face. "I'll wait for you in the car." He would be there, right or wrong, as he always had been. "Thanks, Dad." I glanced at the sky in gratitude. Up the tall steps and through the heavy doors, I walked the long hallway, my damp yellow dress sticking to my back. I sat in a row of chairs outside a conference room. I gazed at high ceilings, inhaled lemony polish over stale air, crossed and uncrossed my legs. Finally, I was ushered into the deans' room.

They sat in a row behind a long, shiny table. Two brown suits and one skirt. The suit with a paunch motioned at me with a flick of his wrist toward a lone wooden folding chair facing the table.

"Sit, please, Miss Schrader," he instructed with a twisted lip that attempted to pass for a smile. I sat down with a thud. He adjusted his half-moon glasses and frowned at some papers. *Are those my grades?* I wobbled, then pulled myself up straight and tugged my dress hem down. My hopes rested on the woman. Her gray hair was tightly permed like an older, wiser mentor's might be. *Surely, she will be on my side. These are enlightened times of Women's Liberation.* I crossed my fingers.

The skirt's words came out clipped, forced through her nose. "Hello, Party Girl." She showed me her crooked teeth. A drop of sweat that had gathered at the nape of my neck cut loose and rolled down my backbone.

One year before, 1966. The day began as students and parents filed into dorms, depositing piles of suitcases, young faces looking forward, older faces turning back. Sad goodbyes, worried wishes. Those moments marked the beginning of my adult life, my well-earned escape from the all-encroaching restrictions of home.

I roomed in a girls' dorm on the third floor with my best friend. We were known as *Schrader and Stilson*. We'd greeted each other by our last names ever since we'd established our *best-friends-to-the-end* loyalty in junior high.

Stilson was a small dark-haired curvy Dane, while I was a tall blonde sylph-like German. You couldn't miss us coming down the street. Now we were about to leave our mark on U-town.

That first afternoon, as we settled in, a siren broke the air. Girls squealed. I glanced up from unpacking as a chant reverberated through the girls' dorm rooms. It gathered power as more voices joined in.

"Panty Raid! Panty Raid!"

String bikinis and low cuts, pinks and blacks, fluttered past the windows. I grabbed a handful of purple silk from my suitcase, ran to the window, and launched it. I stuck my head out to follow the twirl of ribbons and lace into the open meaty paw of a boy on the sidewalk. He was staggering, wolf-whistling up into the air, clutching a Schlitz beer in one hand and my unmentionables in the other. I ducked back in so he wouldn't see me, all the while hoping he had. *So, this is college*!

Our first dinner in the cafeteria, we sized up the other girls: possible friends and probable nots. Afterwards, Stilson and I sprawled across our beds, in the middle of half-emptied suitcases, piles of clothing and books, as I cuddled Ralvue, my raggedy childhood bear who could fit into the palm of my hand.

We were decked out in our floor-length nighties, hers a geranium-red, mine a pastel flowery muumuu from my mother. I had taken scissors to the large ruffles cascading down the front. My heavy wet hair was wound tight around large orange juice cans.

After dissecting the dorm rules and various girls' looks and levels of cool, we reverted to our favorite topic of conversation: *What should I do about Bill?* Bill was my high school boyfriend, still halfway in and out of my life. In months to come, we would exhaust this topic thoroughly.

I bemoaned his infidelity. "I know he was with Sarah Leitweiller. Her sister told me."

"Leave him, Schrader. He's no good for you."

I sighed. "I know. But he's so cute..."

Then *lights out* was announced. Hallways dimmed, the lack of sound from the other rooms was just too obedient. Our chit-chat hushed as we considered our next move. In complicit challenge to our dorm mother, Sheila, we poked our heads out into the hallway. Her door was closed. We smiled at each other, nodded our heads toward the hallway, and tore out of our room and into the elevator.

"Ride it!" was our call. Pushing every button, we rode it up and down. At each floor we announced the floor number in shrieks, ran out, gave a rebel yelp, and escaped back in before the doors closed. How bold we were! How disobedient! This brought side-splitting screeches until we had to clutch our stomachs and wipe our tears. As we neared our floor, the pièce de résistance beckoned. We needed one more act of defiance to satisfy our primal cravings. In unison, we hiked up our nighties and shrugged them off over our heads. Shocked by our boldness, we bolted down the hall stark-naked, our nighties flying out behind us. Safely back in our room, disbelief and exhilaration heated my blood. As our laughter subsided, my stomach clenched. *What was happening to me?*

I surrendered to the frenzy of newfound freedom with dizzying glee. When my family arrived at the end of my first year to gather me up and take me home, rather than greeting them with open arms and packed bags, I was out at the Kollege Klub drinking beer.

When I finally showed up at my dorm room, my outraged mother stood with arms akimbo. "You can't even show up on time? Where were you?"

Grandma Lala waited with saintly patience on a chair just outside my room. My Dad, with firm mouth and furrowed brows, silently paced the room as I shoved my clothes and belongings into suitcases. I had just enough beer on board to find the situation hilarious, but I knew better than to allow a burp or a snort to pass through my lips.

The terrifying trio of deans looked down their noses, with calculating, condemning eyes. I stretched my dress hem down toward my knees. It inched back up. I was yet another wild child who had failed to keep up my grades in freshman year at university. Clearly, I'd had too much fun. But I loved learning. Why had I sacrificed my future, thrown away this gift of higher education?

The paunch parted his twisted lips. "Miss Schrader, your records indicate that you consistently missed several classes while your grades fell from A's to F's. There is no indication that you sought counseling or tutorial help, and all the while you ignored attempts from the university to communicate with you. Your refusal to make an effort to improve your situation exemplifies an attitude of careless indifference. Perhaps some form of rebellious disrespect? What were you intending as your grades plummeted? That all would be forgiven, just that simply?" By this point, his glasses had slipped down his oily nose and rested above his flared nostrils. He shoved them back up with his middle finger.

My brain turned to mush under his onslaught. I struggled to hold on to reason. I had no redeeming argument. Every accusation leveled at me was true. My first year at university was poetry, music, laughter, parties, making out, sleeping in, skipping classes, and devouring pizza at 3:00 am. I cleared my throat.

Now the skirt joined in. "We are waiting, Miss Schrader. Respond, please." She pursed her lips and strummed her lacquered nails on the tabletop.

I squirmed with inadequacy. "Please give me a chance to prove that I can be a serious student." That was it; that was all I had.

The suits and skirt sneered in unison. They weren't having it. The room seemed to sway and buckle as if under water. I was drowning. I struggled for breath. I was banished without flourish, with a cursory closing of my file.

Numbed by this unanimous slap of rejection, I stumbled out of the room, holding back tears of deep regret. Had I thought they would see through my irreverence? Glimpse my true, honorable self, when even I couldn't fully recognize myself?

The hallway was twice as long on my way out. I suspected that the terrible trio had made their decision long before I sat down with them. Perhaps our meeting was nothing but a formality, allowing them to sniff around for a final shred of evidence against me. To pat themselves on the back. I was certain my unlucky yellow dress had sealed my doom.

My footsteps fell heavily on the wooden floor as one of the hallway doors opened. A balding, bespectacled man stepped out.

"Are you Julie Ann Schrader?" I managed a numb nod. He introduced himself as Dean Rothwell. Kindness radiated from him. I compliantly followed him into his office, my legs trembling.

"I see that you earned exemplary grades at Horlick High School. Honor roll. Accolades." I longed to say something brilliant. My uncooperative mouth remained as completely closed as a clamshell.

He continued, "University life can be overwhelming. Did this happen to you?"

Heat filled my face, my eyes stung. His was the voice of my guardian angel. I might have heard a celestial chorus of hallelujahs. My head, loosed by a slim sliver of hope, bounced up and down.

The benevolent dean and I forged an agreement. I would take night classes for two semesters. Solid A grades would deem me worthy of reinstatement. I was once again resurfacing. Breathing.

I left his office a repentant and grateful child, buoyed up by Dean Rothwell's blessing: a second chance. As I floated down the walkway to meet my Dad, I swore a solemn oath upon my lucky yellow dress: Next year I would return with solid A's in my hip pocket.

Trades Day In Quitman 1942

William Carroll Moore

Trades day was coming up in our nearby town of Quitman and I was excited to be going along. My sister Helen would be staying home and minding our little brother Alder, and I would ride to the event with my parents in the green Dodge. Trades day was when we would make the Saturday drive to Quitman or Heber Springs to shop for items unavailable in our small village of Pearson. I had been to two shopping days before and thought they were great fun. I even got a Nehi orange drink each time.

As we took to the road, I had the back seat to myself and watched the landscape passing by, waiting in anticipation of the Burma Shave road signs I knew would appear about halfway to our destination. We were all fans of the signs, and each family member had their favorite one. I liked all of them I could understand, but had memorized my favorite one:

Past schoolhouses / Take it slow / Let our little / Shavers grow / Burma Shave.

We discussed each of our favorites. Sis's favorite we knew was:

The answer to / A maiden's prayer / Is not a chin / Of stubby hair / Burma Shave.

Mother's favorite was:

> *His tenor voice / She thought divine / 'Till whiskers scratched / Sweet Adeline / Burma Shave.*

Dad's favorite I couldn't understand at first, but he explained it and helped me memorize it:

> *I proposed to Ida / Ida refused / Ida won my Ida / If Ida used / Burma Shave.*

We were still laughing about our favorites when the signs appeared, all hoping there would be a new one we hadn't already seen. They assigned me to read them off, and as they appeared I read:

> *Maybe you can't / Shoulder a gun / But you can shoulder / The cost of one / Buy Defense Bonds.*

We were silenced for a moment or two, coming down from the rollicking joy of quoting our favorites. "The war has ruined everything," Dad said, "Even the Burma Shave signs." He and Mother exchanged glances.

Arriving in town, Mother and Dad separated to complete their shopping, and my role was to "help" Dad with his purchases. Mother's list included dress patterns, fabric, and thread, hoping to find the newest, most fashionable patterns which followed the images in the magazines. Sometimes she couldn't find dress patterns in her petite size, but selected the next closest size available and made the necessary adjustments. As a skilled seamstress, she could work wonders with her treadle-operated Singer sewing machine. A few of her usual household supplies were on the list, including castor oil, Mercurochrome, gauze, and surgical tape for our many scuffs, cuts and bruises.

She also bought some powdered chocolate for making desserts and rock candy to reward my sister and brother for enduring our absence.

I went with Dad to the harness shop to pick up a new bridle, and to the general store to buy medications for our livestock and kerosene. He stocked up on his smoking tobacco, the Prince Albert brand. I loved the tin box it came in, shaped flat to fit into a pocket. The tin was a rich color of red with a full-length image on its side of the prince in a long coat and carrying a cane. Another popular brand was Bull Durham, which was packaged in a cloth drawstring bag with a round paper tab on the strings. Dad was disdainful of this brand, saying "Bull Manure" would have been a better name for it.

Trades day was also an opportunity for socializing and exchanging news with friends, neighbors and acquaintances.

Dad and I joined a group of men gathered outside the general store. They were discussing crops, the war, prices and their health in their soft, slow voices. Almost all wore a fresh, white, newly ironed shirt with chino beige trousers, while a few wore their denim bib work overalls. They greeted one another, asking how they were. The answers came in terms of cotton grades used when selling cotton, *fair to middlin'* being one of their favorites.

I was becoming bored and took hold of Dad's chino pocket. "Dad, can I have a nickel to buy some candy?" I looked up to see it wasn't Dad.

The man smiled down saying, "I'll just refer you to your real Dad, young sir." I got my nickel, but was embarrassed, and wished I was tall enough to see faces better.

As we stood there, someone noticed an elderly man walking along the other side of the street and commented, "There goes old man Jenkins. I thought he was long dead."

Another said, "Nope. He's still much alive. I expect he might even stamp the dirt in on all of us."

Laughter and joking were always a part of the conversations. Much of the discussion on this day, however, was about the war. Some of the men talked about their sons or other relatives now in the military. Dad mentioned our own family members in uniform, mostly younger cousins, and wondered out loud why we were in Europe anyway, fighting someone else's war.

I later thought that, absent the war, each of the men might have assigned a higher cotton grade to his and his family's health and welfare.

As the crowd of visitors started thinning out, we loaded the Dodge with our purchases. Sharing the back seat with our supplies, I arranged to sit on the right side so I could easily read the Burma Shave signs again on the way back. But I somehow knew the joyfulness of the signs we felt before today's Burma Shave message was now gone.

After reading the signs again, Dad said to Mother, "The best luck I've had in this life, aside from finding and marrying you, is that I was too young for World War I and too old for this one."

Mother was thinking of her young brother in the military. "I'm just hoping Erben will be okay."

We rode the rest of the way home in silence.

Poetry:
Off the Vine

Stolen

Amber Lea Starfire

I stole a poem the other day
hanging in the sun to dry
waving its bright red vowels
undulating Os and As and Es
deep purple consonants that
tanged like luscious lemons
on the tip of my tongue

I could not help but reach out
pluck that poem
and when I did
its gravitas lay heavy in my palm
emanating aromas of sorrow
a scent of imagination
hastening my hunger

I gobbled it greedily down
in pieces and in whole
every alliteration
every assonance
pure pleasure titillating

senses sharp with locutionary
satisfaction

Even now the poem lingers
fusing synapses, forming bridges
a verbal vivacity of
rhyme and rhythm
jubilation and desperation
animation and expiration
all potential, possibility

I stole a poem the other day
or maybe
the poem stole me

Clown Bird

Barbara Toboni

I spot you across the way
on a parallel path
Are you strolling with me
from yard to yard
you leggy stretch-necked
white winger

Surprise
you swoop and land
atop a rooftop
dwarfing a small house
So comical

Or how about the day
you made a spindly
spectacle of yourself
on the median strip
of Highway 29
What were you thinking
Trying to hitch a ride

Perhaps you
find humans
amusing
as we travel about
tucked into
our wheeled vehicles
peering at you
through glass

I have to laugh
you always seem
to show up
when I find life
too serious

Oddball egret
Clown bird

How Quickly Life Can Change

Carole Malone Nelson

A glass of famed Burgundy in hand
end of a perfect day.
A barge trip through French wine country.
Life doesn't get better than this.

Lounge chairs beckon from forward deck
hot air balloons rise like brilliant flowers
from grassy field.
Not a care in the world.

My eyes slowly close,
breath deepens, cleansing
whooshing sounds are all I hear.
A smile creeps across my face.

Crew member gently taps my shoulder
gives me a handwritten note.
Call home, it reads.
My heart begins pounding.

What awaits can only be bad.
1990, no one calls you in Europe,
or owns a mobile.
Not even the barge has a phone.

Short ride in rickety school bus
under skies beginning to dim.
A dark cafe in nearby village
the only long-distance phone.

Bright orange phone
owner dials a dozen numbers
sad voice answers on first ring
utters only two words.

How quickly life can change.

Wildfire Elegy

Dana Rodney

I used to think I could rely on the days
one following the other so faithfully
the innocent breath of morning
the folding petals of night
the years flowing by
like rushing water

Nature's mood is generally predictable
except for the periodic cataclysm:
a meteor annihilating dinosaurs
tectonic plates colliding
and depositing a mountain range
But you never think of a cataclysm interrupting
your own placid days
You never think
you are the dinosaur

You never think about how
you are just carbon rearranged
something combustible
how everything you've collected in a lifetime
is just more fuel to a flame

That delicate painting of orange poppies
I hung on the wall wherever I lived
consumed as greedily
as a forgotten sock under my bed

My mother's thumb-stained recipes
a lover's penciled poem
that nut-brown guitar that played a thousand songs
the carefully-tended jasmine
my old cowboy boots stained
with the sweat of my youth

Even my mother's ashes that rested on a shelf
now twice burned
mingle in the rubble.

Now I no longer belong to a place
The objects that housed my memories have combusted
I alone am left to remember the things
When I thought the things would be left to remember me.

What Are Possessions?

Edgar Calvelo

Everything around her is silent

Because she is deaf she uses hand-voice
Words she cannot hear but can see

Every word she loves
Every word is a poem

Love can create a wreckage
Indifference cuts affection

Imagine a glacier breaking
A giant sound she cannot hear

Her hands voice catastrophe
Your eyes paint the scene

We don't have to possess everything
To live forever

Sometimes we don't have to be heard
Be seen.

Absence can assert a presence
Asking herself abstract questions.

With sign language
She shapes and shakes the world.

Like once when I crossed a river while I was blinded by the sun
I found strength from calm waters.

War

Emily Freiman

There's a war going on outside me they say
Always a war keeps us fear-crouched
This is not a fly to bat away
This is an intelligent invisible enemy
Headliner on Nextdoor: Someone's Throwing A Party!
Online neighbors begin to bicker
That got the war started separation into small mobs
Others in heightened fright aim suppressed anger point fingers
declare partying selfish ignorant dangerous
Come to your senses slow the spread shelter in place
We're in this together

There's a war going on inside me I say
Makes digesting breakfast a toe-curling challenge
Being afraid, and being afraid of being afraid
Then letting go letting faith hope surface
Am I alive today because of God
Am I dead tomorrow due to behavior of others
Losing touch of another sentient being
Someone something dear
Losing sanity my delicate balance

There's a war going on inside and out we say
Closer now in our face leering
Spreading death among us
Somewhere someone is being born living
dying right this minute
Viruses do their thing invading is their nature
weeding out the sick infirm unhealthy
Of course we rage against the night fight to be here
rally forces do our best
Because there's always
War

They Told Us About Snow

Jeanne Powell

Here we dwell happily on our mountain
enveloped in gardenias, jasmine,
eucalyptus and begonia
for most of the year, too besotted with joy
to wonder about others or wander
in search of them, those mythical others,
said to exist in climates less forgiving.

Every other lifetime or so we are surprised,
no, startled by refugees from harsher worlds
who wander in with grim intent, focused
only on escaping what they know. Shivering
in disbelief and delight, they huddle together
to gain the warmth of courage to glance about.

Their fear melts as we approach their
chilly limbs and seek to dissolve their
preoccupation with coldness of recent lives.
As reserve thaws and their blue images
relax into warm brown, these refugees
began to speak and tell us about snow.

Mystery of Mustard

It appears quickly mustard
grows a February bumper crop
painted across vineyard landscape
sunburst of vibrating color

just when you think Meyer-lemon hues
are here to stay little orange tractors
mow flowered plants between rows
to enrich soil sow future seeds

Abraham's descendants numerous
as stars in sky sand on seashore
cycle swings life to death to life again
our essence returns nutrients to the soil

one generation flows into its following
flowers die to burst forth again
return living to its cosmic spark
within vast intricate realm of nature

as mowed mustard lies loose in vineyard
tall-eared jackrabbit darts across trail
first brilliant orange poppies appear
yet aura of golden blooms remains.

The Courage of Grief

Joan Osterman

He pierced her buoyant heart, took her for weak—
assailed her in Bergdorf's, laughed through the aisle.
Grief gathers courage yet struggles to speak.

Tethered to secret scars—fateful, unique
shackles that smothered her voice with his bile—
he pierced her buoyant heart, took her for weak.

Advised in private, no justice to seek—
in public, E. Jean flashed her trademark smile.
Grief gathers courage yet struggles to speak.

Taking flight on her breezy wit to peak,
acclaim soared high, of her singular style.
He pierced her buoyant heart, took her for weak.

E. Jean's truth in print—no rumor oblique—
revealing the rape, disclosing his guile.
Grief gathers courage, gets ready to speak.

Despite denials, DNA did leak
onto the black wool dress, he did defile.

He pierced her buoyant heart, took her for weak.
Grief gathers courage, steps forward to speak.

E. Jean Carroll's memoir *What Do We Need Men For?*
and MSNBC interview 6/28/2019 inspired this poem

Luna Luna Vella Moon

Lance Burris

Luna luna Vella moon,
a foggy night in early June.
Bella bella luna moon,
your yellow light dispels the gloom.
Moona Moona hooting owl,
tuxedo cat is on the prowl.

Vella vella quarter-round,
falling down on old Sonoma town
where a cheese shop can be found
selling cheeses by the pound,
bear flag stamped on every round.

Cheesemaker with rolled up sleeves,
your sample plate is meant to tease.
Take my order, if you please:
"A quarter-round of hard jack cheese."

Luna luna Vella moon.
Bella bella luna moon.
Moona moona hooting owl.
Tuxedo cat still on the prowl.

Ol' George

Lisa Burnett Toller

Grandpa picks his way
carefully through ancient granite
planting his feet firmly as he
retraces steps of his childhood.

Memories hang in the air
like milkweed
we liberated from their pods this morning.
He retells the adventures of his youth with an occasional chuckle
as we climb ever upward
through towering sugar pines and lichen-covered cedars.

He's eighty now and needs to stop and rest more often.
Three decades younger, I struggle to keep up.
I think about trails he's hiked
streams fished, campfires patiently stoked.
The high Sierra calls to him still.

This is the place I will bring his ashes
when his days are done.
He can rest beneath pine trees near Eagle Creek,
where rushing snow melt
carves hollows in boulders
smooth as bones.

Breakers

Madeline Wise

to know a need
to seek an ocean
a constant love of
life in motion
sustaining visions
buoying mind
fleeting moments
held in time

curving
curling
joining
escaping
drawn somewhere
beyond
a need revealed

feeding mystery
ever changing
reaching out
reaching in
living movement

ebb of sea foam
envelopes my feet
knowing the gesture of
coming
receding
returning

I Love You Song

Marianne Lyon

I want to write a feverish *I love you* song
serenade you, watch your agate blue eyes
flicker open, find myself inside of them
your astonishing smile lays warm on me

I want to write a fierce *I love you* song
a raw opening legato
when years, days, hours together
minutes slow, hungry seconds linger

I want to write a fairytale *I love you* song
of pianissimo evenings gazing out window
moon and sun, one rising other setting
blending into strangeness like a dream

I close my eyes, conjure a melodic tremolo
will a romantic verse, but of course
you are laughing fortissimo over back fence
with neighbor, when a lento of silence intrudes

I begin again to fashion a possible lyric
But become stunned when your percussive stride

drums through front door, down echoing hall
bids my eyes open to your half-moon grin

Your smile thick with sustained passion
moist lips staccato-touch mine
I lift my chin with soft andante
beg for lingering encore

Storm

Nathaniel Robert Winters

Evil clouds
Attacks sky
All over the world

Infected inhabitants
Quickly put up
No Vacancy signs

People hide away
Caught in science fiction plot
Afraid to go anywhere

Nefarious virus infects the living
Like nothing this century
Schools sit empty

Pestilence
Of biblical proportions
Seize world-wide population

Ich Bin Ein Berliner 1963

Peggy Prescott

Berlin is a surprise, an assault
of newness and neon after
months of touring treasures
sooted with centuries of history.

This Berlin, at least this rebuilt half
with its glitzy American style, seems
to show a strange deference to the power
that had bombed away its past.

I am curious about the other side,
that strange unknown world where
our arch enemies the evil Communists
live, plot the insidious Cold War.

Seeing the Wall is chilling, a stark reminder
of divisions man creates over and over.
I approach the gate with trepidation,
my first experience of an armed guard.

My two friends are nearby
but for this moment it is only the guard
and this twenty-year-old me who quickly
notices he is so young, so good-looking.

He takes my passport, checks it out carefully,
then checks me out carefully and says
with a charming smile and surprisingly good English
"And how are you today, Miss Peggy?"

I smile right back and tell him
"I'm great, but my feet are sore."
He laughs and his smile broadens.
"Ah, yes. Mine too from so much stand here."

Suddenly we are both laughing
and in that moment there are
no walls, no divisions. We are just
two young people in Berlin.

Two-Week Vacation

Joanne Jagoda

The father, broad chested with muscled arms
sweats through his sleeveless undershirt
curses in German under his breath
cramming suitcases into the old Plymouth
for their two-week family vacation.

The mother, a pony-tailed beauty,
thinks she looks fat in her new blue-checked pedal pushers
white blouse tied under full breasts—latest style.
The kids stay clear when she's in her "mood,"
slamming cupboards, doing last-minute stuff.

Never ready when the father wants to *hit* the road
they're not speaking when he pulls out
into San Francisco fog, thick as mother's barley soup.

At the toll booth, the kids skirmish
over who gets to hand the man the quarter.
The girl, twelve, frizzy haired
says it's her turn because it's always her turn.
Gangly, awkward, she has yet to ripen
hates everything about herself.

The boy sitting shotgun, ten, short and freckled
whispers he hates his sister's guts.
She hisses, "you're stupid,"
and kicks his seat with her Keds.

The mother grimaces, her headache starting.
The boy fiddles with the radio;
the father yells "turn it down for crying out loud!"

Johnny Mathis comes on, the father sings
along to *Chances Are,* catches his wife's eye
through the rear-view mirror and winks
but she ignores him.
The kids make loud farting noises.

When they reach Sonoma
blessed sun breaks through the fog shroud.
The mother smiles, the father exhales.

Purple Mountain Majesty

John Petraglia

I've seen it often before
maybe never so much as this evening
Napa's Mt. George
round-topped in the near distance
dusky glory, dark lavender
plum-colored even
in shadowy mountainside recesses.

It's no Pike's Peak, mind you
Colorado's 14,000-footer
that inspired Katherine Lee Bates 125 years ago
after crossing Kansas' amber waves of grain.

But it's plenty purple, tall enough
to remind me of her aspirational lyrics
for a beautiful America.

Then in lilac melancholy
at times minor rage
I think how far we've strayed
so detached, so offset
from her fruited plains

her shining seas
to the bully privilege
of our nation's leaders

alienated neighbors
ourselves

to where now no God
would shed on us, his grace.
when we may need it most

Toloma Crossing

Kathleen Herrmann

First light stretches across summit
Toloma springs over rugged boulders
Dodges tangled manzanita
Mirrored eyes dart

Below thin shadows cling to serpentine road
I climb
High on rain-cleansed air

Blurry projectile erupts from thicket
Landing on all fours
Furry head pivots
Hypnotic gaze fixed on me
Scanning my mortal coil

Soon to be a big cat
Dilated pupils tick with data
Black-tipped tail curls and flicks
Strength drains from my limbs
Adrenaline floods the pause between jagged breaths
Paralyzed in the crosshairs of scrutiny

Standing taller
Do I appear threatening?
Or does mama peer through the brush
Spring-loaded?

Behind me
Faint hum crescendos to a growl
Cold sweat
Beat up Honda rumbles past
Unlocking our feral stare

She recoils
Bounding away to waking hills
Where Esselen footfalls linger
And the spirit of Toloma wears many faces

Slow exhale
Searching for the elusive edge of her shadow
I walk on

Aunt Lottie

Barbara Toboni

Mom to daughter
at the family reunion
If I could have given you anything
I would have given you an Aunt Lottie
Lottie dressed her best
Impressed her nieces
with the highest heels
finest scarves
and kindest ruby smile

Shall we go for a drive
my darlings
Allowed us to root
through her purse
daub her Evening in Paris
chew Juicy Fruit gum

She had an affair
with a married man
We girls didn't know
the city's fire chief

Explains the long rides
by way of the fire station

Hodgkin's disease
stole her from us too early
On good days
Aunt Lottie still dropped by
high heels teetering
nylons sagging
lipstick applied with a poke

People talk
I'm sorry Aunt Lottie

Enough

Emily Freiman

At my computer August afternoon in Napa
Five months into extraordinary threatening Covid times
A parching breeze billows blue embroidered curtains a tad then more.
Billowing sheer fabric waves slowly sensuously
Letting me know that wind will traverse
Threshold from out there to inside small apartment
Crossing boundaries with nary a may I is it safe

We are requested to live in the world yet
distance ourselves from what matters
Neighbors cannot blithely sweep into my domain these viral days

Home most of the time days pass as a dream
Sanctuary for the introvert smilingly seated inside
One day into another watercolor on brush changes a line
tweaks a hue here and there
in complex scene delicately drawn painted well
Keeping same foundational security soothes a wary spirit
Memory of passing person light touch close breath reminds me

If I compare too deeply life's similes before the muffling mask
my carefully constructed shelter will dissolve
So I don't ask yet wonder
Is it enough

Toni Lights And Baldwin Lamps

Jeanne Powell

When the poorly lit room is
too small for deep breathing
when the road is too steep
and rutted for safe walking

I search for Toni lights
and Baldwin lamps
to make the journey bearable
to give hope enough

To allow me to forgive
those who do not wish
to hear my voice or
witness my face

Inhaling Toni Morrison
chanting James Baldwin
sheltered in their armor
I walk on, wrapped in joy

Turning Seventy-Four

Jim Mc Donald

Sun rises on chilly late-fall morning
I wake to murmur of breaths
room in focus my wife beside me
body still moves mind clear
start another year I say
to hell with talk about aging move on

Every year without knowing
I pass the day when
light will fail final breath expires
Should we celebrate birth or passing?
Time cyclical linear compressed
expanded merges into my dreams

Sweet bird sounds accompany
sunshine streaking through curtains
I welcome another day on earth
speck in vast history of time
cycles light to dark to light
continual creation ruin renewal.

inspired by WS Merwin

"It Is What It Is"

Carole Malone Nelson

She stared through the window of the tour bus
at aging, colonial Salvador de Bahia
with the same melancholy she feels today
when she looks in the mirror.
Rio Olympics months away
Brazilians attempted to restore classic buildings
with heavy coats of vibrant paint.

She gathers her arsenal of makeup brushes
amused by a harsh, obvious reality.
No amount of colorful paint
or facelifts
could restore those architectural wonders
or her
to their beautiful youth of long ago.

Though centuries older, those iconic ladies
displayed the same parched surfaces
and weakening interiors
that plague this septuagenarian.
Her crepey skin, their worn facades

weathered by a lifelong love-affair with a cruel,
abusive lover tropical sun.

Today she readies for her 60th high school reunion
like every day, hiding behind a heavy coat of makeup.
Each day her armor takes a little longer to apply
yields fewer noticeable results.
Often, she is grateful for dimming eyesight.
After stroking the final bright layer to chafed lips,
she smiles and turns away from the mirror.

"It is what it is, " she says to herself.

And it ain't what it was.

Toward Evening

Madeline Wise

I walk late in the day
light beckons me to come
when shadows are at play
down a path of glowing sun

toward the western mountain view
strolling curves with gentle bends
I continue to renew
a road of hope that does not end

pausing moments lift in sound
whispering breezes pass my cheek
lighter steps return me home
settling time in evening ease

Star Words

Marianne Lyon

A gleaming universe lives inside books
so much luster spread over pages
ignites my eyes with luminous delight

Tonight they blink on one by one
like house lights at dusk
medallion then *solitaire*
sparkler follows *virtuoso*

Soon begin to dazzle in pairs
dance duets, wink approvals
silver twirls *glitter*
celestial bows to *majesty*

Cluster whirls my gaze to incandescent
flashing its way out of eventide
diamond tiara crowns inky night
phosphorous rosary implores darkness

As if pinged on my earlobe
I hear sounds like a bell, like a trill
sonorities take on word shapes

minstrel messenger meanders melody
moored mesh merry-go-round

Scents drape cool around me
more words blossom
pine-glow, wildfire char, mossy luster

Wisdom phrases like this
they lessen the blackness we carry
fall from some heavenly lexicon

Stars words debut faster
not like angry avalanche, shouting crowd
but like an orator dropping luminarias
from his night sky podium

Music of the Woods

Peggy Prescott

I step out of the chilled cabin
head to a bed of soft, dried pine needles
lean against a smooth boulder backrest.
I close my eyes, smile at the sun.
A deep slow breath fills me
with gratitude for this pine-scented
paradise, makes me think of
my morning meditation…
feelings thoughts emotions … release
I realize mental chatter
is gone already, let bird songs fill
my head. I try to place their notes
on a treble clef, marvel at
percussive monotone from one
steady 3-1-1 from another
intermittent soprano counterpoints.
Heavenly, this music of the woods. I do not
even worry about the black bear that ambled
through here last week. Surely, if he
comes back, he will lie down next to me
whisper "It's wonderful, isn't it?"

Savory, Sweet

Joan Osterman

Wedding photos show a woman and a man—
fortyish. He beams through a blond beard;
she, a cascade of auburn curls. Second marriage
for both. They fill each other's empty nests.

blooms, ripens into a fine merlot,
blackberry with undertones of cloves, cocoa.
Lacking the raw edge of young wines,
but fuller, more complex, satisfying.

With the zeal of youth and the endurance
of middle age, the two climb Glacier Point,
wander Yosemite, listen to the roar of the falls,
where he kisses the mist from her cheek.

They tangle over trifles, bicker
through the day. Tangoing their quarrels,
they lunge, twirl apart, pull together.

Vitriol—uninvited—dozes in the corner.
Without fertile soil to develop roots, it withers,
allowing tenderness and trust to blossom.

Arthritic now, the husband shuffles down
the driveway, struggles to collect their empty
trash cans, refuses help from the neighbor
who flirted with him, not long ago.

The lovers drive scenic routes, stop at vistas.
Find boutique hotels perched on cliffs
overlooking the Pacific. Dine on the balcony,
lulled by rhythmic waves, energized by salt air.

A current portrait shows her with white curls.
He smiles through a gray beard. Underpainting,*
the luminous red-orange of poppies, evokes
their bond—still strong, still vibrant.

Tunnel at Bitterroot Mountain

Kathleen Herrmann

Tires grind over gravel
where lumber trains once rolled
Tunnel yawns its invitation
We pedal under broad arch
switching on slender beams of light

Boisterous hoots boomerang inside
smiles masking concentration
chilled air clings to tanned limbs
daylight dims behind us

Filaments of light scatter
dancing across cave-like walls
extinguished by thickening velvet shadows

Pupils dilate
fingers grip
pedals lock
wide swerve
I'm eight again
Daddy, don't let go

Just in time
third eye opens
in the fourth dimension
I see my child self-sail
by
perched upon seat
focused
fearless

She can
I can
go

Distant white pixel punctures black surround
I race toward it
gray gloom peeling from my back
I lift my face
Look at me, Daddy

Happenstance

John Petraglia

No one noticed
the literary serendip
including non-member me at first
when passing Vintner's Golf Club
bulletin board
a summer's worth of Mondays
during weekly tee times.

Club championship bracket pairings
on bright-white chipboard
for all to see
who plays whom and when
advancing inexorably
to fleeting Yountville glory.

But there it was
in black magic marker
neat Arial-ish hand
in a second-round contest

Wallace
v
Cunningham

<u>Alvarez</u>
<u>v</u>
<u>Stegner</u>

And as if to prove
randomness sometimes
brings the familiar
Cunningham and Alvarez
obliged syzygy
losing their matches
perfectly aligning
the memorable third-round contest

<u>Wallace</u>
<u>v</u>
<u>Stegner</u>

Eminence gris of western literature
Stanford Professor
father of *Angle of Repose*
Big Rock Candy Mountain
long-favored *Crossing to Safety*
with its binding friendships
heartening rescues.

Mr. Stegner
your estate might realize
a well-deserved uptick in sales
from this well fated happenstance
or not.

A Day in the Life

Edgar Calvelo

Eager to walk to the river
Not because I want to see her again
The woman with a yellow parasol
But for little things along the way:
Silent birds, spider webs, shifting shadows, a muse
Thoughts scattered in illumined landscape
Lined by sycamore, birch, maple, oak
A place different from other places
Everyone wishes a "someplace to be."

Today I am watching from the riverbank
Leaning on a tree trunk
Listening for breath in the wind
To gather emotions concealed in parentheses
The flowering of sheltered hours
In dark contagious spaces.

The river gleams, flows with stories:
Sea otters, submerging and surfacing,
Frolicking, oblivious of surroundings,
Making each other happy

My eyes catch festive new arrivals
Moving colors: yellow, red, green vests,
Kayakers glide the river
Paddle to the edge for their destination

Egrets inattentive to the river, chase each other
Awkward in their twig-like legs
Their wings glitter, soundless, brushing the grass as they
run Teasing, flirting in the open field
One of life's last frivolities.

I try to concentrate, frame the spectacle
Pain on my side is heavy, malignant
Like roots welded to bones
Wordless messages between synapses
Incremental intrusion that rarely diminishes
Like lessons of eternity.

There are days I stand, like a tree inside a storm,
Rain, whipping wind, lightning, heavy thunders
Without forsaking sacred hours deep in my being

Experience gives me hope
Honoring with gratitude others
Who taught me courage and forgiveness,
Repeating prayer of faith and perseverance.

Tomorrow is Thursday, a day of elation
I am dining with a friend.

Contributing Authors

Contributors

Kathleen Andersen is a retired physician living in Napa who enjoys writing, painting, and making noise with her quartet. Her memoir is developing in fits and starts, mostly fits. She is grateful to her local writing group, art friends, and teachers for their advice, support, and encouragement.

Stephen Bakalyar, during his diverse career as a chemist, wrote marketing materials and published research papers in peer-reviewed scientific journals. He writes poems, essays and short stories. He is a member of two branches of the California Writers Club, and enjoys reading his work at their salons and open mics.

Lance Burris is a fifth-generation Northern Californian who lives in Napa. After a long career in large-scaled real estate development, he retired and committed himself to writing and painting on a full-time basis, activities long pursued apart from his profession.

Edgar Calvelo is a retired physician. He has taken classes in creative writing at Jackson Community College in Michigan and Napa Valley Community College. He enjoys playing chess. He tries to walk to the river every day, carrying a book and stops to sit at empty benches along the way and read. He lives in Napa with his wife.

Marilyn Campbell spent her time during Covid-19 writing poetry and short essays about garden pests and acts of civil disobedience— subjects not that different if one thinks about it. She has published two historical novels: *Trains to Concordia* and

A Train to Nowhere. She is a frequent contributor to anthologies and small journals. Visit her at www.CamitzkePress.com

Penelope Anne Cole writes award-winning children's books, poetry, and short stories for adults—in California Writers Club's Tri-Valley, High Desert, and SF Peninsula branch anthologies, and in San Mateo County Fair's Literary Stage's "Carry the Light" anthology. Like her cats, she writes creative non-fiction memoirs about her many lives.

Brien Crothers is a native Northern Californian, who makes his home north of the Napa Valley, in Hidden Valley Lake. He is a world traveler and adventurer. Once, while trekking in the Swiss Alps, he came across a pink church in a tiny village in a long valley.

Emily Freiman, a painter and writer, facilitated a writing/arts course, "Invite the Muse", from 2017-2019. She's an AANV *"Palette"* newsletter editor, and she designed a logo for the NVW newsletter, "DeVine Write". Some publishing plans of hers are a volume of poems written during her Art Therapist years, and an "Invite the Muse Course" facilitator handbook.

Rebecca Levy-Gantt, DO, is an OB-GYN for over 20 years, and is currently practicing in Napa Valley, California. Her private practice is Premier OB-Gyn, Napa Inc. She published a book called *Womb with a View: Tales from the Delivery, Emergency and Operating Rooms.*

Stephanie Hawks is a retired string specialist with N.V.U.S.D. She lives in Middletown, Ca. where she and her husband Edward are building their home.

Kathleen Herrmann has published poems, nonfiction articles, and has taught young writers. Adventure, nature, people and current events inspire her verse, as well as the evocative poetry, prose, storytelling, and improvisation of fellow writers.

Lenore Hirsch writes poetry, essays, and short stories. Her books include her dog's memoir, *My Leash on Life*, a poetry collection *Leavings*, and *Laugh and Live: Advice for Aging Boomers*. She is currently writing a novel about the adventures of a middle school vice-principal. See www.lenorehirsch.com www.laughing- oak.com

Kymberlie Ingalls is native to the SF Bay Area. She is a pioneer in personal blogging. Her style is loose, experimental, and a journey in self and emotion. Works include personal essay, prose, short fiction and memoir. Beware of occasional falling opinions.

Joanne Jagoda, after retiring in 2009, one inspiring workshop launched her on an unexpected writing trajectory. Her stories, poetry and creative nonfiction appear on-line and in numerous print anthologies. In 2020, Joanne published, *My Runaway Hourglass, Seventy Poems Celebrating Seventy Years*. She has spent time in Calistoga her entire life. www.joannejagoda.com

David Kerns, a retired Stanford medical professor, has been a columnist and feature writer for the *Napa Valley Register* since 2011. He has written two published novels: *Standard of Care* (2008) and *Fortnight on Maxwell Street,* which won the 2018 Eric Hoffer Book Award in the General Fiction Category.

Sue Kesler, author of three tongue-in-cheek series, *My Partner Jakup the Jay, J&R Rides Again,* and *Jaybird in a Lei.* Starring an unlikely detective team, *Blue Talon*, an urban fantasy about a boy from Imperial Russia murdered by the Cossacks who does not die, and *Haw Kola,* a teen story set in 1860 about an historical incident in Minnesota.

Thomas Kincaid is a Napa native and a lifelong writer. He has published several stories in various publications, including *Temper* magazine and the *University of Southern California Anthology*.

Geoffrey K. Leigh taught and published research in academia for 30 years, including a co-edited book. He now works locally in residential real estate. He self-published a book, *Rekindling Our Cosmic Spark*, published a poem and story in *Meritage*, and recently completed his second novel of a trilogy.

Sarita Lopez has been a member of Napa Valley Writers since 2015 and is now President, Publicity Chair and Newsletter Editor of the club. She published her first YA novel, *Fauxcialite*, in 2016, and her second YA novel, *The Last Pageant in Texas*, in 2019. She is currently working on her third novel.

Marianne Lyon has been a music teacher for 43 years. After teaching in Hong Kong, she returned to Napa Valley and has been published in various literary magazines and reviews. She was nominated for the Pushcart Award 2016. She has spent time teaching in Nicaragua. She is a member of the California Writers Club, Solstice Writers in St. Helena California. She is an Adjunct Professor at Touro University Vallejo California. Marianne Lyon officially became *Napa County Poet Laureate 2021,* on March 9, 2021.

Juanita J. Martin, First Poet Laureate of Fairfield, CA, 2010-2012, is author of The Lighthouse Beckons poetry book. She's a member of Ina Coolbrith Circle, Poets & Writers, and Redwood Writers 2007-2017. She's widely published in poetry and nonfiction, and active in Napa Valley Writers, where she started writing poetry book reviews. Juanita J. Martin wrote her first memoir and flash fiction story, as managing editor for Third Harvest 2021 anthology. www. jmartinpoetwriter.com

Jim Mc Donald retired from his career as a podiatrist in 2014 and began a creative journey as a writer and painter. He lives in Yountville, CA and chairs the Yountville Arts Commission.

William Carroll Moore is a retired architect/urban planner living in Napa. After earning a BS in Architecture at UC Berkeley and a MS in Urban Planning at Athens Technological Institute in Greece, his professional career included technical writing and teaching at California Polytechnic State University in San Luis Obispo. He writes fiction, creative nonfiction and poetry.

Paul Moser has been writing reasonably seriously since 2007, and has self-published four books: *The New Revised Cataclysm, T- Bull and the Lost Men, Inside the Flavor League: A Slightly Buzzed Satirical Novel, Seeking: An Encounter with Spiritual Ecstasy and Its Aftermath.*

Carole Malone Nelson has lived in the Bay Area since entering U.C. Berkeley in 1959. She and her husband now live happily in Napa. In retirement they've traveled to 38 of the 50 United States and to well over 100 countries. She recently published her second book, a traveler's memoir, titled: *What in The Word Are You Doing Here?* That she hopes will both entertain and inspire others to get out of their bubble.

Joan Osterman grew up in Philadelphia, then transplanted to Northern California. She writes poetry, memoir, and fiction. Her poetry has been published in Napa Valley Writers anthology *Meritage*. She has presented her poems at the *Meritage* book launch and other venues, including The Sebastopol Center for the Arts.

John Petraglia is a Napa writer, poet, and former environmental communications professional. He has completed a children's picture book manuscript and is moving it towards publication. For ten years, he was a docent at Robinson Jeffers Tor House. Originally from NY, he dabbles in wine, food, travel, art, hiking, running. jsapet@gmail.com

Dr. Jeanne Powell holds degrees from WSU, Michigan and USF, California. Jeanne is a poet and essayist, with four books in print from Taurean Horn Press and Regent Press: *My Own Silence, Two Seasons, Word Dancing,* and *Carousel.* She founded Meridien PressWorks, which published 20 writers in 20 years. Jeanne's film and cultural reviews appear online. Jeanne's new collection of poetry will be published in April 2021 by Taurean Horn Press. jeanne-powell.com, starkinsider.com/author/jeanp

Peggy Prescott retired from elementary school teaching and began taking classes with George Stratton. She has won multiple awards in the Jessamyn West Contest for fiction, non-fiction and poetry. She studied with Carl Dennis, Brenda Hillman, Jane Hirschfield and Peter Ho Davies at the Napa Valley Writers Conference and meets regularly with the Solstice Writers Group in St. Helena. Her book *Neurotic's Guide to Retirement* was published in 2010.

Dana Rodney is a single mother and small business owner in St. Helena, CA. She began writing in 2018, concentrating on poetry and novel-writing. Two completed novels are *The Butterfly Wing* and *The Warming.* Dana is currently working on a third novel, *The Law of Is.*

Julie Ann Schrader is a psychotherapist, published author, and teacher. She describes herself as a lover of words. She has been writing poems, songs, and stories since childhood. For Julie, writing is a form of self-reflection; a way to collect herself and to simultaneously put herself aside. Julie has authored a novel of historical fiction, memoir pieces, poems, and short stories. She is drawn to mysticism, magic, and dreams. Her website is www.julieschraderauthor.com

Amber Lea Starfire is an award-winning author, editor, and writing coach with a passion for helping others tell their stories. Her published work includes two memoirs, *Accidental Jesus Freak* and *Not the Mother I Remember,* as well as several books on the art of journaling. See her blog and online courses at www.writingthroughlife.com.

Barbara Toboni is a writer, blogger, and poet. She has published a variety of short stories and articles in anthologies, journals, and online. Barbara is also the author of three collections of poetry and a children's picture book, *The Bunny Poets*. Read more about her at www.barbaratoboni.com

Lisa Burnett Toller's background in marketing honed her observation of human behavior. In addition to writing poetry and personal essays, she writes stories for children. As a mother, grandmother, and a reading tutor for elementary school students, she loves to watch a child's delight in a good tale.

Nathaniel Robert "Bob" Winters despite having Parkinson's disease, writes most days. The Vietnam Navy Veteran earned a BA in history from Sonoma State and an MA from CSU Stanislaus. The retired teacher lives with his wife in the Napa Valley. In eleven years, he's published sixteen books, poetry and prose.

Rose Winters is a writer of sci-fi/fantasy, coming of age fiction, memoir, short stories, poetry, essays and screenplays. A professional musician by trade, she is a published songwriter, including Ray Charles' *Spirit of Christmas* album cut, "Christmas in my Heart".

Madeline Wise writes fiction and poetry. She is a member of Solstice Writers and Napa Valley Writers. Her work has appeared in *American Fiction Vol. 13, North Atlantic Review, Evening Street Review, San Pedro River Review, Coneflower Café,* and other journals. Madeline lives with her husband in St. Helena, California.

Michael Wycombe originally trained as a hard scientist and was on the academia track to become a professor when he discovered computers back in the 60s, which brought him to Palo Alto. After years in high tech management, including CEO, he moved to Napa in time for the latest earthquake.

About Napa Valley Writers

www.napavalleywriters.net

Today, with 68 members, Napa Valley Writers continues to flourish and thrive through gifts of friendship, professional contacts, and the craft of writing. Napa supports its writers in various styles, genres, in various stages of their writing careers and other writing-related fields.

Napa promotes personal and professional growth through critique groups, workshops, monthly speakers, meetings, salons, open mic events, and publications. Member pictures and bios are promoted on the website and writing-related articles, stories and poetry are promoted through our monthly newsletter.

Every two years, our club publishes an anthology of our member contributions of short stories, memoir, and poetry. This is yet another way our members are promoted and celebrated for their writing accomplishments. Our third anthology, *Third Harvest 2021*, along with copies of *Meritage* and *First Press*, are available for sale. See the newsletter and website for more information.

Members work with the wider community on projects such as the one with the Rail Arts District. Members mentor writers of all ages. Our club will support educational programs and offer scholarships for the advancement of literary endeavors throughout the community.

Napa Valley Writers is always looking for ways to improve service to our members.

Our members are from the Bay Area to Napa County and beyond. We strive to promote an appreciation of art, history, literature, reading, writing, and the expansion of our club.

Are you thinking about joining Napa Valley Writers? Napa Valley Writers are steeped in the Napa Valley Wine Country. There are many things here to see, do, and write about. If you want to join Napa Valley Writers, go to www.napavalleywriters.net and click on the membership tab.

—**Juanita J. Martin,** Managing Editor, Third Harvest 2021

Made in the USA
Middletown, DE
19 February 2022